MISS ABERNATHY'S CONCISE

SLAVE TRAINING MANUAL

Miss Abernathy's Concise

Slave Training Manual

by Christina Abernathy

greenery press

Published in the United States by Greenery Press, 3739 Balboa Ave. #195, San Francisco, CA 94121.

The publishers thank Lee Hawaii for his help in making this book a reality, and Lee Hawaii thanks Lady Petra for teaching him more about submission and slavery than he was even sure he could cope with at the time.

Cover illustration by W.S. Fisher, P.O. Box 17387, Seattle, WA 98107.

ISBN 9-9639763-9-7

ISBN 0-9639763-9-7

51195>

9 780963 976390

CONTENTS

to
H. Marwood
and
C. Parker

PRELUDE IN D

She is coming to my home tonight for the first time. We have met before, but only in public, at cafés and art galleries. She always arrives before me, not wishing to be late, but she waits patiently for me to arrive. She leaves me the most comfortable seat.

But tonight, she is coming to me, to my home, to serve me. I have given her clear instructions: she must arrive on the dot of eight. Under her conservative business suit, she will wear white stockings and garters; she will carry high-heeled white pumps in her bag. She will wear no jewelry, for tonight, I will adorn her.

When I hear the cautious knock at the door, I do not rise. I call to her; she enters, closes the door behind her. Not once does she turn her back on me. I am watching.

I gesture for her to approach me, and she does, on her hands and knees, crawling gracefully across the floor. She stops within hand's reach and folds her body neatly, legs tucked under her and palms upturned on her thighs. Her head is bent, and her long hair falls forward, away from the nape of her neck: her beautiful, naked neck. I touch her and she shivers. I lift her chin with my finger and trace her collarbone with my gloved hand.

"Why are you here?"

"To serve you, Mistress." Her voice is soft and light and only trembles a little.

"You agree to obey me and to let my will be yours for this evening, as we have discussed?"

"Yes, Mistress. I would be honored, Mistress."

A lovely touch, that last. And I know I have chosen well this time.

I reach for the collar, the smooth metal links that will appear so heavy on her slender neck. She wants to follow my hand with her eyes, but I have not given her permission to, so she waits as I have left her.

"Kneel up!"

She raises herself up so that I can reach her more easily. I push her hair back over her shoulders and then gesture for her to hold it up. I can see the pulse in her lovely throat as the metal chain encircles it like a hand.

"As long as you wear this collar, you are mine to command. And until I remove it from your neck, I will consider you my responsibility, my possession, my slave."

She shudders almost imperceptibly.

Tonight she has come to me. And she is mine.

INTRODUCTION

*In which we strive to make a good beginning by
defining our terms and setting out our plans.*

Gentle Reader...

Perhaps you picked up this book out of mere curiosity, a slender volume like many others on a bookstore shelf. Or perhaps the title caught your eye, the words "slave training" flashing out like a beacon. Perhaps you have fantasized about dominance and submission for years but thought that masters and slaves only met in badly written paperbacks. Perhaps you are a dominant in search of a slave. Perhaps you are a submissive who yearns to serve but does not know where to begin. Perhaps you are a more experienced person in search of a detailed discussion of slave training, as distinct from other types of dominant/submissive play.

Consider this a primer, a simple and concise manual of consensual dominance and submission. It is not a pornographic novel, nor is it a directory of professional dominas. It does provide some background information, a reading list, a history lesson or two, and, at its heart, a simple program for training erotic slaves.

What Is "BDSM"?

Before we begin, it is vital that we define some of the specialized vocabulary used when discussing slaves and their training.

BDSM is a convenient shorthand for several overlapping terms: B/D refers to "bondage and discipline"; D/S to "dominance and submission"; and S/M to "sadism and masochism." While different people mean different things by these terms, for the purpose of this book, we shall define them as follows: bondage and discipline, as the name implies, refers to a wide range of activities including physical restraint and "punishment." It sometimes involves fantasy role-play. Sadomasochism covers all of the physical techniques that produce intense sensation, and the enjoyment of same. Dominance and submission refers to a consensual arrangement in which one partner takes the lead and the other follows that lead. It generally involves some form of role-play, and may or may not make use of bondage, discipline, or S/M techniques like whipping. There are many excellent introductions to BDSM available; if you are unfamiliar with the basics, check the resource guide at the end of this book.

What BDSM Is Not

Critics of dominant/submissive lifestyles like to remind us of the atrocities committed against human beings under the name of "slavery," from the ancient Greeks on down to the United States in the 19th century. Because of its historical resonance, many people find the very term "slave" offensive.

The distinction between BDSM and barbarism can be summed up in one word: consent. To avoid confusion, I reserve the term "slavery" for the sort of violence visited on African-Americans, among others, in the seventeenth, eighteenth, and nineteenth centuries. When speaking of consensual erotic submission, I use the term "slavehood." I prefer the word "slavehood," because it expresses a personal vocation rather than a social institution.

Some people enjoy fantasy role-play in which their chosen roles parallel historical types: plantation owner and black slave, or Greek prince and captive barbarian warrior. Again, the key word here is "chosen." We are talking about consenting adults making rational, informed decisions about their own lives. For submissives who fantasize about being owned or possessed, these roles may provide the ultimate satisfaction. Real slavery is illegal, as is pandering; erotic role-play, despite the efforts of the religious right, is not.

Just as BDSM is not about literally owning human beings, it is also not equivalent with abuse, sexual or otherwise. If you have any questions regarding this assertion, please reread the paragraph on consent above. If you still have questions about this topic, read one or more of the introductory books listed in the resource directory before proceeding.

How Is D/S Different?

What distinguishes dominance and submission from other types of BDSM? If you accept the premise that the brain is the largest human sex organ, then BDSM is truly a mind-game. In the case of dominant/submissive play, this is doubly true. For unlike S/M or B/D, D/S is essentially a question of mind over matter. No elaborate dungeons or sex-toy collections are necessary. Instead, both the dominant and the submissive bring their intelligence and will into play. Submission depends on the individual's ability to align his will with that of the dominant and to use his intelligence to fulfill her wishes gracefully and efficiently. The dominant, for her part, must be ready and able to direct the submissive's will with her own.

Dominant/submissive relationships are role-based. A role-based relationship is, as the term suggests, one in which the dynamic between the partners is dictated by their chosen roles. The roles constitute the essence of their union, insofar as those roles are chosen to express the qualities in each that bind them, one to the other. Examples of role-based D/S relationships are Mistress-slave, Head-master-schoolboy, or Trainer-puppy. A role-based relationship is by nature ongoing, but it can encompass everything from the occasional weekend scene to a full-time contract.

This program focuses on the practical training of personal slaves. It presupposes that not only does the dominant enjoy the simple act of commanding obedience, but he also has specific needs. Floors to be swept. Meals to be prepared. Boots to be polished, or worshipped, or both. In other words, the type of D/S interactions described here have service at their heart.

Now that we have our definitions in place, let us turn to the matter at hand.

PART ONE:
THE TRAINING PROGRAM

*In which we examine the specifics of
training an erotic slave.*

Attitude

While the actual training of a slave encompasses the total
person, the *sine qua non* of a service-oriented submissive is the correct
attitude. Different roles may dictate different training techniques,
but all slaves – and dominants, too, for that matter – should cultivate
an attitude of mindfulness.

For our purposes, mindfulness may be defined as an over-
arching awareness of one's person, surroundings, and circumstances.
It is a gentle attention, focused but not forced. Many spiritual
traditions recommend sitting, chanting, or other forms of meditation
to awaken a mindful state. For the slave, it is dharma yoga, the
pursuit of one's true vocation, that is the path to mindfulness. A
slave's mindfulness should encompass her physical body, her mental
awareness, her emotional state and, insofar as it is possible, the physical,

mental, and emotional state of the dominant and any other person in the environment.

This is not to say that a slave must be clairvoyant or an empath; she must first cultivate self-awareness, and under tutelage, awareness of the dominant's needs and wishes. Experienced slaves do often develop a sort of sixth sense, the ability to anticipate the dominant's needs before he verbalizes them.

The Interview

How can a dominant determine the best sort of training for a would-be slave? Before being accepted for formal training, a submissive should be interviewed by the prospective owner. The interview is an opportunity for both parties to learn something about the other's expectations and needs, to ask questions, express concerns, and generally familiarize themselves with the workings of the other's mind. The submissive may have questions about the dominant's style of training and interests, and the prospective owner should take care to answer these as honestly and directly as possible, to avoid any misunderstandings or unwitting deceptions. The dominant should be aware that submissives are often hesitant to ask direct questions and often must be prompted to do so. If the dominant maintains an attentive but relaxed demeanor, he will help put the submissive at ease.

To determine a submissive's suitability for training, it is vital that the dominant have extensive information about the person. Such information includes, but is hardly limited to, the following:

- ℀ the slave's full legal name and address
- ℀ all existing medical conditions and a general medical history
- ℀ any required medications and their whereabouts (it is wise to lay in a supply of them at the dominant's home or wherever the training will take place)

ରୟ emergency contacts and limitations to same, such as doctors, family members or friends, and therapists, and how much or how little personal information may be revealed to them in the event of an emergency

ରୟ any psychological limitations to play, such as abuse or incest history

Other information may include fantasies, sexual history, attitudes about submission, desires and preferences, and any interesting details a dominant may uncover during the interview. It is appropriate to take notes and keep a written record of the proceedings, but the dominant should encourage the submissive to speak freely, as one may learn as much if not more about a person by listening as by watching. Be alert for physical and verbal signs of ambivalence or hesitation, fear, or apprehension – pausing, blushing, hedging, or squirming. These are not necessarily indications that the submissive is unsuited for service, but they provide excellent opportunities for the dominant to explore areas that the submissive is not consciously aware of, or is ashamed of. It is remarkable how little attention people pay to their own speech, particularly when they are excited and nervous. By listening carefully to a submissive during the interview, the dominant can later create the illusion of being a mindreader or of having "secret" information about the slave.

A series of interviews should be conducted before any arrangement is made or contract signed, and at regular intervals thereafter. For an ongoing contract, once a month is reasonable. Both parties should be given ample opportunity to gain the necessary information to make an informed decision about the training. The results of these interviews should be kept in a file in a locked box, along with a copy of the contract and any personal documents relating to the slave. A contract should include a clause specifying whether this file will be turned over to the submissive in the event that the relationship ends, whether the dominant may keep a copy of some or all of the information, and to what extent such information may be shared with others (when negotiating to bring another dominant into the scene, for example).

It is appropriate for the dominant to request from experienced submissives a sort of résumé of service previously provided or at least a list of references. Likewise, submissives should be provided upon request with the names of those who can vouch for the dominant's credibility.

The dominant may also require other documentation from the submissive, such as letters of petition, fictional narratives of the submissive's fantasies, journal entries (see below), or verification of the submissive's qualifications for specific forms of service, such as a valid driver's license and clean driving record from a prospective chauffeur.

It should be understood that such preliminary interviews, while expressive of a mutual interest in training, do not imply any obligation on the part of the dominant to take on the submissive, nor on the part of the submissive to accept any training program offered.

The Slave Journal

Slaves-in-training should be encouraged to keep a written record of their thoughts, fantasies, and experiences. The journal is usually the property of the submissive but is meant to be read by the dominant. Thus, the dominant may require that the slave address the journal directly to her and that special written forms be followed.

For example, it is common for slaves to use the lower case when referring to themselves and to capitalize all references to the dominant: "Mistress, i am writing this journal as You requested. i hope it meets with Your approval." Or, they may be required to omit the first person pronoun altogether: "this slave is writing a journal as You requested." Some dominants find the use of the possessive in reference to themselves highly offensive, as the Mistress does not belong to the slave. They feel it is more appropriate for a slave to speak of "the Mistress" than of "my Mistress." Holding to this pattern can result in some interesting linguistic difficulties, but greatly encourages mindfulness. It is to be used at the dominant's discretion. Entries should be made in the journal on a regular basis (anywhere from once a day to once a week has proved useful). The dominant may wish to respond, verbally or in written form, to the entries.

Other Written Training Assignments

In addition to the slave journal, the dominant may assign essays on specific topics of interest, such as the history of erotic servitude or tea service. Book reports on BDSM classics have proved edifying (see appendix A for a selective reading list). The dominant may uncover a hidden talent for verbal expression – a useful and attractive attribute in a slave – that he may want to further encourage. At very least, he will have better insight into the submissive's thoughts and frame of mind.

Physical Preparation

Slaves should be encouraged to care for their bodies so that they will be better able to serve the dominant and so that such service will be more pleasing. Many dominants require that their slaves shave off their body hair, either just the pubic hair, or all of it. The feeling of nakedness and vulnerability this simple change can produce should not be underestimated. Men often find shaving their body hair humiliating, particularly if they associate shaving with women or femininity. Reactions like these provide an excellent opportunity to uncover unexamined prejudices that the slave may carry. Prejudices are an unnecessary burden that is best laid aside as quickly as possible. The slave will need his strength for other, more pressing matters.

The dominant may also require that the slave give herself a cleansing enema or douche as a preparation for service, or the dominant may wish to administer the enema herself. In either case, make sure that the enema is administered properly, with no additives, warm but not hot water, and low water pressure. Commercial preparations can be used in a pinch, but water is most effective and is unlikely to cause unpleasant reactions. (Some individuals add a small amount of salt to help prevent undue fluid absorption.) Soaps and any form of alcohol should be avoided. The nozzle should be well lubricated with KY Jelly or some other preparation and should be inserted slowly and carefully, as the rectum is quite sensitive. Begin with a small amount of water (a pint or so). Over time, the slave will be able to hold more, although for practical cleanliness, no more than a quart is necessary. The "gallons and gallons" of water referred to in some pornographic literature should remain in the realm of fantasy.

If the slave suffers from hemorrhoids or rectal bleeding, or if these conditions develop at any point during training, she should inform the dominant, who must take great care not to aggravate the condition by requiring too-frequent cleansings. These common conditions can be easily treated by a health care professional.

The slave may also arrange her hair according to the dominant's wishes, use cosmetics (rouging the nipples and vulva, for example), trim or grow her nails, and so on. In all cases, such modifications should be undertaken, not out of vanity, but with the awareness of the dominant's wishes in mind.

Control of the Body

Some dominants take great pleasure in controlling the bodily functions of the slave. As long as such control does no damage to the slave's health, it is acceptable. Sade wrote a notorious passage in which he describes the ideal diet for a slave of a coprophiliac: stewed chicken and rice. While Miss Abernathy does not condone the ingestion of feces, for reasons of hygiene and health, the concept of such intense bodily control is not unpleasant.

It is a sad fact that many submissives, so adept at caring for others, neglect their own well-being. Part of a dominant's task in training such a person is to instill good habits in matters of food, sleep, and exercise, and not to encourage self-destruction. If the dominant notices that the slave is remiss in matters of self-care, he should take steps to remedy the situation. This can be accomplished from within the scene. For example, the dominant may wish to reward the slave for taking care of herself by allowing her to eat the same food as he does, perhaps leaving a little on his plate for the slave to enjoy. (Of course, she may be required to eat it without utensils while crouching on the floor.)

The dominant may also control the submissive's sleep, speech, and excretory functions, but great care should be taken not to exhaust the slave or endanger his health with such games.

The question of sexual abstinence for submissives frequently arises. Assuming that the slave has turned this right over to the dominant during negotiation, I believe that a dominant may act with impunity in restricting a slave's sexual pleasure. A state of sexual hunger drives slaves to better performance, and the promise of release is a powerful stimulant. If the dominant finds that the slave is unable to resist the temptation to masturbate, he may want to invest in one of the fine chastity belts or "cock cages" now available.

I am aware of no concrete evidence that sexual abstinence causes any problem other than frustration. Remind the slave that his sexual desire, like all else, is your property and should be dedicated to your pleasure, not the slave's.

Forms of Address

In their speech, as in all else, slaves will find an opportunity to express their respect for the dominant. Most dominants will specify a default form of address, such as "Master" or "Mistress," "Sir" or "Madam." While in service, the slave should always use this honorific when addressing the dominant. If no default form is specified, the dominant should specify a form at the beginning of a training session, perhaps during the collaring ritual. He may say, "From this point on, you will address me as 'Master'." He should expect the slave to reply, "Yes, Master." If such an acknowledgment is not forthcoming, he may prompt the slave. Dominants should be vigilant with forms of address; the slave should use it every time she addresses the dominant. Omissions should be noted and corrected. Nothing is more disappointing to a submissive than an inattentive dominant.

If a slave has become adept at one form of address, the dominant can up the ante by requiring a more complex form, such as the repetition of the honorific at the beginning and end of an utterance: "Master, may I please worship your boots now, Master?"

Honorifics can be simple or complex. They may or may not include a name. For example, a slave who is serving two masters, one to whom she is contracted and one who is only visiting the household, may address "her" master simply as "Master" and the other dominant by the honorific and his given name: "Master Jack."

An additional note on names is in order. Some dominants, especially professionals, use a "scene name" instead of or in addition to their legal or street name. Likewise, some submissives entering the community choose a scene name, and dominants may occasionally give their submissives "slave names." Individuals have different preferences regarding the use of scene names. I once heard a professional dominant at an S/M community function say, "Oh, please, call me [her given name]! We are all friends here; this is no dungeon."

Other professionals prefer to keep their given names private, for legal and personal reasons. When in doubt, ask. No one will fault you, and you will avoid awkward misunderstandings.

Positioning the Body

One of the most obvious ways that a slave can express his submission is through his body. A slave should strive to be graceful and unobtrusive at all times. Just as he should keep his mind focused on the task at hand, so he should eliminate unnecessary gestures.

The dominant should instruct the slave to assume a default posture when at rest. The most common postures are kneeling and standing. To assume the kneeling posture, the slave should fold his legs neatly beneath him. The knees may be held together or spread apart, according to the dominant's wishes. Hands may rest palm up or down on the thighs, may be clasped lightly at the small of the back, or the fingers may be laced behind the neck. The head should be inclined forward, the eyes cast down. Be aware that most Westerners are not accustomed to long periods of kneeling, so this posture may cause some discomfort. Slaves with existing knee problems should, of course, be given another posture to assume.

In the standing posture, for example, the slave stands erect with feet together or slightly apart. Hands are again clasped lightly behind the back, either at the base of the spine or at the waist, or they are left hanging loosely and gracefully at the sides. If the arms are at the sides, the slave should take care not to ball his hands into fists, but to let his open hand show his willingness to serve. Again, the head should be inclined and the eyes down. (In some exceptional cases, such as military training, the eyes may be kept up and forward.)

The slave should practice these postures under the direction of the dominant until he can execute them perfectly. He may then be shown "his" spot, the default location where he should assume the "at rest" posture when a task has been completed and he is awaiting further instruction.

In addition to the "at rest" posture, the slave should be made aware of any physical restrictions placed on him. Is he allowed to sit on the furniture? May he use utensils to eat? May he walk from place to place, or should he crawl? When, if ever, is it permissible to look the dominant in the eye? The dominant must reflect upon these details and inform the slave accordingly. Whatever the dominant's decision, she must be consistent. Unless her intent is to confuse and frustrate the slave, the dominant should stick to her own instructions when correcting a slave.

Many novice submissives find it difficult to hold still for any length of time. Often this has nothing to do with physical problems, but indicates a lack of awareness of the body. Jiggling legs, tapping fingers, nervous coughs, and wandering eyes are to be discouraged. Instruct the submissive to focus his attention on his breathing and make a slow mental sweep along the full length of the body, taking note of any points of tension and relieving them. The submissive should also be instructed in basic stretches and encouraged to perform them regularly. This discipline will greatly increase a slave's capacity for maintaining postures.

Again, vigilance is paramount. Submissives expect correction and are often crushed when the dominant fails to notice an error. Such sloppiness undermines their confidence in the dominant and makes them question the sincerity of the dominant's commitment to them. The dominant's actions should always reinforce the slave's submission.

Voice Commands and Postures

A slave should learn to respond immediately to verbal commands. Some commands are so frequent and simple that a word or two should elicit the desired effect. We have already covered the first two postures, kneeling and standing. Several more useful postures follow.

"Come Here"

The dominant uses this command when ordering the slave to approach. The slave is expected to take the most direct route possible without disturbing any other people who may be in the area. She should either walk swiftly and gracefully to where the dominant is, or she should drop to her hands and knees and crawl there. Often the circumstances will dictate which method is appropriate. In a non-kinky setting, crawling will only cause scandal; likewise, a gravel path will damage the slave's knees or rip her clothing. When the slave reaches the dominant, she should stop within arm's reach and assume the "at rest" posture while waiting for further instruction.

She may also be expected to acknowledge the dominant verbally, as, for example, "You require me, Mistress?"

"Go"

This command is used when sending a slave to attend to a task or when the dominant wishes the slave to leave the room or area. The slave should again move quickly and gracefully. The key, however, is to do so without turning his back on the dominant. Slaves must learn excellent observation skills; when entering a room, they should already be planning the most efficient way to exit it.

"Follow" or "Attend"

This command tells the slave to follow the dominant as she moves about. Again, the slave is expected to crawl or to walk, although under most circumstances, walking is more efficient. When asked to "attend," the slave should be prepared to assist the dominant in other ways: by carrying packages, holding bags or drinks, fetching ashtrays or footstools, and a myriad of other small tasks.

"Present"

This command indicates that the slave should make her body available to the dominant in a pre-arranged fashion. The most common posture is kneeling with the legs spread wide and the pelvis tilted up, exposing the genitals. Hands should be lightly laced at the back of the neck, with elbows out to the sides. The shoulders should be thrown back to accentuate the breasts. Alternatively, the slave may be expected to kneel down on hands and knees, legs spread and head down, giving access to the posterior.

Another variation is "present for punishment." The dominant may also specify "present ass" or "present thighs" or whatever portion of the anatomy she intends as the recipient of her correction. Here the slave kneels down, pressing the top of the body flat against the ground and lifting the posterior into the air to receive the blows. Alternatively, he may lean across a table or other flat surface with his legs spread apart.

"Open"

A related command is "open," upon which the slave should assume a position of sexual availability. The specifics of the posture depend upon the dominant's preferred way of using the slave. For women, this may mean a hands-and-knees posture like the second "present" option; stretched out on the back with legs spread; kneeling with mouth open; or bent over a convenient piece of furniture. For men, the hands-and-knees posture and the kneeling posture are appropriate for oral use; the slave may also be expected to lie on his back to be ridden.

"Down" or "Prostrate Yourself"

Upon hearing this command, the slave should lie flat on his belly in front of the dominant. His arms should be stretched forward over his head and his feet should be pressed flat so the soles are exposed. The forehead should touch the floor. This posture may be used for abasement, confession, or as a prelude to worship.

"Worship"

Here the slave should worship whatever object or body part the dominant offers. Worship is generally understood to be oral, using both lips and tongue, unless otherwise specified. Worship should always be respectful, never greedy or sloppy. Nothing is more offensive than a slave who drools on a boot or slobbers on a dominant's hand. Consider that the lips and tongue express the totality of the slave's devotion during worship. Sometimes a dominant will allow the slave to cradle the object or body part in his hands, or will rest it on his shoulder, as when a Mistress rests her booted leg on a slave's shoulder to allow better access to the top of the boot or to her sex.

Basic Forms of Service for Slaves

In addition to being able to execute the basic positions described in the previous section, slaves should be able to perform some basic tasks. Not all of the tasks listed are appropriate for every type of slave; dominants can pick and choose at their discretion.

Housework

The amount and type of housework a dominant may require will vary with the dominant's living situation and personal standards of tidiness. Whether she lives in a small apartment or a cavernous mansion, the dominant will need the following:

- ෬ floors swept and washed (and possibly polished)
- ෬ rugs vacuumed and possibly cleaned
- ෬ surfaces and objects dusted
- ෬ counters cleaned
- ෬ dishes washed, dried, and put away

- laundry washed, dried, folded or ironed, and put away
- simple meals and beverages prepared

If the dominant has specifications for any of these tasks – whether socks are to be folded or balled, the proper proportions of sugar and milk in tea, which china to use for guests and which for everyday – she must make them very clear to the slave, or she will be disappointed. Slaves, for their part, ought always to ask how to do a task if they are unsure, rather than doing it incorrectly and wasting their own time and the dominant's by having to do it again. It is also the dominant's responsibility to provide the necessary tools and supplies for any household cleaning task.

Errands

Almost everyone has at some time wished that the groceries would magically appear in the cupboard. Slaves should be prepared to do basic grocery and sundry shopping for the dominant. In preparing a shopping list, the slave should note the dominant's preferred brands and should inquire about specialty items like coffee, tea, chocolate, liquor, and unusual bath products. The dominant should make arrangements to pay for the goods in some simple way: a presigned check, an ATM card from a household account, or cash. The slave may be expected to shop within a budget, and efforts toward economy should be rewarded.

A slave can do many other simple errands: dropping off and picking up dry cleaning (be sure to provide the slave with the claim check ticket); going to the post office and retrieving the dominant's mail and packages from a post office box or mail drop (make sure the slave has the key or make arrangements with the postmaster in advance); returning rented items, such as videos or cars; picking up forms at the DMV or insurance companies. Remember that many large cities have droves of "professional organizers" who make their living running errands for busy people. Your slave is a valuable resource.

If the slave will be driving, she should be able to produce a valid driver's license, registration, and proof of insurance for her vehicle. If the slave will be using the dominant's vehicle, be sure the insurance covers other drivers. The slave should be responsible for any parking or traffic tickets incurred, and should be firmly chastised for such irresponsible behavior if she in fact gets one.

Personal Attendance

A slave should be ready to fetch and carry the dominant's possessions or to deliver messages to third parties. The dominant should instruct the slave in basic grooming and clothing care, and may expect the slave to trim or style her hair, provide her with a manicure or pedicure, or even apply her makeup. Slaves are often responsible for drawing baths and attending the dominant while she bathes. The slave should be able to press clothing and do any basic mending – hemming, buttons, and the like – that may be necessary. If the dominant wears leather shoes or boots, the slave should know how to clean and polish them.

Sexual Techniques

If the slave has been engaged for sexual use, he should be trained to perform whatever type of sexual service the dominant most enjoys. A sex slave should always be prepared to be used, and should make sure that the necessary supplies – condoms, latex gloves, lubricant, and such – are at hand. This may mean carrying a supply on his person, or secreting caches away around the house. Spontaneity is no excuse for unsafe sex. Nor should the dominant allow his demands to endanger the slave or himself. As one dominant of my acquaintance is fond of saying, "If you break your toys, you don't get to play with them anymore."

Special Skills

Any of the basic skills described above can become the focus of a slave's training. A simple maid may become an expert in household management and advance to the position of housekeeper. Similarly, a slave who shows a talent for personal care might be sent to study massage or hairdressing. Sex slaves can train in techniques of special interest to the dominant, such as fisting or Tantric breath. A slave who shows a special talent in the kitchen can train as a chef. Open schools like The Learning Annex offer many classes for a nominal fee, from wine-tasting to stripping, that the dominant may wish the slave to attend. Copies of any certificates or transcripts from such classes should be duly added to the slave's file.

Voice-Training

Voice-training is a specialized area of accomplishment that many slaves never approach. At its simplest, voice-training involves teaching a slave when it is appropriate to maintain silence (which is most of the time) and when and how to speak. This type of training is usually part of any basic program. In its more advanced form, voice-training requires practice in reading or recitation or other types of vocal performance, and is useful for slaves expected to entertain at social functions. It may also refer to training a slave to respond to dominants in a way that avoids references to the self or to the slave's own preferences or will. Responses such as "If it pleases you, Sir," or "Whatever Mistress wishes," fall into this category. In its most advanced form, voice-training may include instruction in foreign languages and complex social etiquette, and is appropriate for slaves who will act as escorts or companions to diplomats or businesspeople or who show a special aptitude for and interest in languages. Advanced voice-training requires a commitment of many years and is best reserved for long-term contracts.

Punishment

It is inevitable that at some point in her training, even the most accomplished slave will make a mistake. The dominant should set

clear guidelines for correction of errors. If the point of the punishment is correction, then the rule is, "Let the punishment fit the
crime." In general, errors that indicate lack of consideration for the
dominant or behavior that runs counter to the agreed-upon code of
ethics for the slave should be punished more severely than simple
physical mistakes. Errors of the former sort include the following:
neglecting proper forms of address, disobeying direct commands,
gossiping, arrogance, tardiness, failure to complete a training assign-
ment, disrespect in any form.

Punishments should also suit the slave. A slave who is very
attached to a token may have that token taken away for a period of
time. A slave who consistently forgets honorifics may be put under a
discipline of total silence; this technique is also useful for gossips.
Arrogant slaves may be denied use of the furniture or eating utensils.
A slave who is unduly proud of his appearance may be dressed in
unfashionable or ill-fitting clothes or be denied access to the bath. In
extreme cases, the dominant may choose to send the slave away for a
period of time. Miss Abernathy believes this punishment should be
reserved for only the most obdurate slaves or for when the dominant
feels unable to control her own anger.

In more simple cases, repetition is the key. If a slave cannot
remember how to fold the dominant's socks, it may be time for her to
empty the entire sock drawer and refold every pair correctly. If a slave
forgets to use the lower-case "i" in written assignments, she may be
required to write "i must be humble," one hundred times. Slaves
who lose keys or bus passes may be made to wear them around their
necks on a string, like schoolchildren do. Never underestimate the
power of humiliation.

Physical discipline may prove useful for slaves who are physically
and psychically able to withstand it. Often the mere threat of a
beating is enough to whip the slave into shape. A petulant, whining

slave should be taken over the dominant's knee and spanked like the child he is. A slave who is negligent in his use of honorifics can be required to count each stroke, thanking the dominant in appropriately respectful form. Lazy slaves who are caught sitting around may be paddled so that when they next sit down, their bruises will remind them of their obligations.

Dominants sometimes find themselves at a loss about how to punish masochistic slaves, for whom physical beatings are the purest pleasure. One method is to deny the slave a beating or administer one with a tool that the slave does not enjoy. Another tactic is to use some other form of punishment, such as memorizing a humiliatingly silly poem, or performing some seemingly endless task, like scrubbing the bathroom grout with bleach and a toothbrush. The slave might also be asked to perform a particularly challenging task, as a chance to turn the punishment into an occasion for reward.

Recognition and Reward

Just as a slave's deficiencies must be corrected, her achievements should be duly noted and rewarded. Rewards may be physical – a sensuous beating for a masochist, an orgasm for a sex slave – or material, such as a token or a new uniform.

Privilege: The Best Reward of All

The simplest and often most effective form of reward is privilege. A slave who is allowed greater intimacy with the dominant and a more advanced level of service will feel treasured as the valuable possession he is. Once again, the reward should fit the slave. For a fetishist, worshipping the fetish object to his heart's content may be in order. Likewise, permission to entertain the dominant by masturbating in front of him would be an excellent reward for a slave who has shown exemplary sexual restraint. If the slave is a "switch," that is, if he has dominant tendencies as well as submissive, one great reward may be the gift of his own slave to train.

The Collar

The slave collar remains the most widely recognized mark of submission. As such, it makes an excellent reward for a new slave who has completed her preparations well. One dominant friend of mine has devised a collar system. As his slave progresses through the training program, she is rewarded with different collars, each representing a new level of achievement: first white, then red, then green and so on. (Another dominant might provide medals or badges with appropriate titles. Dominants with a military bent may mark each advance in rank with a "stripe.")

Many slaves crave the collar; some can barely function without it. When a dominant collars her slave, she signals that their roles are in full effect. By accepting the collar, the slave indicates her willingness to serve the dominant at that time. If the collaring is performed publicly, at a play party or other community function, it alerts other players that the slave is unavailable and that the dominant should be approached before any contact is made with the slave.

Collars may be of many different types, from the studded black leather variety to a simple velvet ribbon. Dominants must take great care in selecting the collar, for it is a tangible symbol of their will and their commitment to the slave. The collar should suit the slave's role. A choke-chain is appropriate for a slave submitting to canine training; a delicate lace ribbon may adorn a lady's maid. Submissives who serve in non-kinky public should be provided with a more subtle collar — a stylish silver chain from a jeweler's or even a length of leather lacing in the dominant's signature color — to avoid undue attention and confrontation with potentially hostile outsiders. (The submissive may of course be given a more formal collar for service in the home or at BDSM functions.)

Miss Abernathy has a particular prejudice regarding collars: they should lock. Anyone may wear a collar for casual play or for the sheer fashion value of it, but a submissive in service to a dominant should be given the assurance that a locked collar provides. The lock not only holds the submissive captive to the dominant, but binds the dominant to the submissive. A dominant may wish to display the key as a pendant to remind the slave and any onlookers of her power and love for the submissive. (One note of caution is in order here: all locks should have more than one working key, and the submissive should be informed of the location of an emergency key and the specific circumstances under which he may use it to release himself from the collar. I am speaking of real emergencies here: fire, earthquakes, medical crises.)

Collars should fit snugly without impeding movement or restricting breathing. One exception is the posture collar, which is designed to hold the neck straight and the head forward. They are especially useful for slouching sissy maids or other servants who lack focus. A posture collar should be fitted by a knowledgeable leatherworker to assure that it does not damage the neck, restrict breathing, or chafe the skin. Many dominants prefer adjustable collars, particularly if the slave is expected to do heavy labor or to sleep in the collar. In both cases, the neck may swell, and loosening the collar a notch will prevent the danger of strangulation.

The Collaring Ritual

When being collared, the slave should present herself in a manner that displays her gratitude and willingness to serve. Miss Abernathy prefers a kneeling position with the head inclined, eyes cast downward, and palms resting lightly on the thighs. If the slave is presenting the collar, she should hold it in her upturned hands and, raising her arms above her head, offer it to the dominant, who should not have to bend or stretch to reach it. The dominant may then command the slave to "kneel up" to receive the collar. At this command, the slave rises so that the body forms a straight line from neck to knees. She should raise her head enough to allow the dominant to encircle her neck with the collar.

At this point, the dominant may require the slave to make some gesture of gratitude, such as kissing the collar, reciting a pledge of service, or simply requesting sincerely that the dominant collar her. Then the dominant will put the collar around the slave's neck, perhaps expressing its significance to her and to the slave: "While you wear this collar, you are mine to command. You will obey me without hesitation. And as long as you wear it, I will consider you my responsibility. I will let no harm come to you as long as you are in my care." The dominant may at this time specify her preferred form of address, any tasks the slave is to perform, and any specific disciplines the slave may be under, such as not using utensils to eat or remaining silent.

Submissives, take note: although you may wear it for years, do not make the mistake of thinking that the collar belongs to you. Unless he specifically indicates otherwise, the collar remains the property of the dominant and must therefore be returned immediately upon request. Should the slave choose to lay aside the collar without warning or explanation, the dominant may reasonably assume that the slave has broken contract and no longer wishes to be in service. Naturally, such gestures made without prior communication are likely to cause confusion and hurt feelings and are best avoided. In the matter of collars, as in all things, both the dominant and the submissive are obligated to express themselves as clearly and directly as possible at all times.

Ornaments or Tokens

In addition to the collar, the dominant may wish to reward the slave by providing any number of different types of tokens for the slave to wear. Some leather shops make customized brass, silver, or leather name plates, which can be worn on a jacket, attached to the collar itself, or otherwise displayed on the slave's clothing. Dog tags, both of the military and canine varieties, can be embossed with owner's name, address, and so on. Jewelers can engrave similar information on ID bracelets, rings, or most charming, ankle bracelets, those lovely remnants of shackles. Tokens can be even more subtle. The dominant may require the slave to wear a signature color or to carry a handkerchief impregnated with the dominant's perfume or cologne. Such intimate items provide solace to a slave temporarily separated from her owner. In any case, the token should serve as a constant reminder of servitude.

Permanent Marks

Other slaves may literally earn their stripes: permanent marks to show their accomplishments in the service arts. Just as O first earned the "irons" (labia piercings) and later a brand, a dominant can reward a slave with ornamental body modifications. Such marks represent a deep commitment and should never be undertaken lightly.

It should go without saying that no one ought to be marked without his or her explicit permission. No reputable professional will mark an unwilling person, and neither should a dominant.

The most common forms of permanent marks in D/S relationships are piercings, brands, cuttings, and tattoos.

Piercing

Permanent body piercing has become very stylish in the past few years, with the rich and famous sporting nose, nipple, and navel piercings. For a dominant to give a submissive rings, however, the relationship should be more than a seasonal fashion. Any kind of permanent piercing can have significance as a dominant's mark, but the most common piercings are earlobe, nipple, and genital. The earlobe is convenient, visible, and socially acceptable. Marking may be as simple as the submissive wearing an earring purchased by or belonging to the dominant. The surgical stainless steel rings commonly used at piercing salons can be adorned with a bead in the dominant's signature color. A small engraved pendant with the dominant's initials can be hung from an earring.

Nipple piercings are distinctly more erotic (for most people!) than an earlobe piercing. Sensitivity often increases when a nipple is pierced; also, the nipple spreads. Nipple skin is tough, and provided the piercing is well-healed and the jewelry sturdy enough, pierced nipples can take a lot of stimulation. A sadistic dominant may use this state to her advantage. It may also amuse her to lead her slave around a party by a leash attached to his nipple jewelry or to hang an engraved pendant or weight from it.

Genital piercings are certainly the most highly erotically charged piercings. Not only do most genital piercings increase erotic sensation, but piercing a slave's genitals sends a very definite message: this is mine. O's irons were labia piercings ornamented with her master's initials, but almost any part of the female or male external genitalia can be pierced: the clitoral hood, inner and outer labia, the penis head and shaft, the scrotal sac, the perineum.

Do not try to pierce your slave yourself! All piercings should be done by trained individuals only!!! The popularity of piercing has resulted in many fly-by-night piercers (and dominants) who have only a few days or weeks of training. It is better to go without the piercing until you can schedule an appointment with a reputable piercer than to risk infection and worse. A list of reliable piercers is provided in the resource guide. Piercings have the advantage that they are practical (in S/M terms), they are beautiful, and if the jewelry is removed, they will usually heal over (although rarely without some sort of scar). In the event that the relationship ends, the submissive will not be left with a large or obvious mark that reminds her of her loss every time she sees it.

Other Permanent Marks

The same cannot be said for branding, tattooing, or cutting. While all three have intense erotic associations – O was branded, after all – they are potentially dangerous procedures that, like piercing, should be done by trained individuals only. Some established body modification artists will be happy to perform bonding rituals between a dominant and submissive that center on marking. Contact information for several experienced body modification artists is listed in the resource guide.

In choosing a design for a brand, tattoo, or cutting, a dominant should bear in mind that the submissive may well wear it for the rest of her life. Symbols that are too intimately connected to the dominant – names, initials, portraits – make poor choices. It is much better to choose a symbol of commitment or of transformation, such as a circular Celtic knot or a phoenix. Totem animals or runes are another good choice, since they invoke protection. The dominant may want to explore the art of the slave's particular ethnic group(s) in deciding on a design.

Testing

The dominant may sometimes feel it necessary to test the slave. She may doubt the slave's sincerity or she may want to assess the level of his development in specific skills. In either case, she may choose to create a situation in which the slave will be asked to prove his obedience, honesty, skill, or devotion. If a slave has been studying tea service, the easiest way to test his skill is to invite several trusted friends over for afternoon tea. To test a slave's obedience, ask him to perform a seemingly humiliating or dangerous task (the danger need not even be real). To prove a slave's honesty, ask a friend to tell the slave something unpleasant – perhaps a critique of the dominant's behavior – and then make the slave recount the conversation. Slaves prove their love and devotion at every turn, in the small acts of service that make up their day, but loyalty in times of trouble is the best measure of a slave's devotion.

The principles of testing should be discussed in a theoretical way during preliminary negotiations and consent received. Particularly in the case of a "set-up," like the test of honesty described above, tests may involve mild deceptions, and if the dominant does not admit them, he cannot reasonably expect his slaves to admit their deceptions either.

Other Types of Service

Public Attendance and Play

Thus far we have spoken mainly of private service in the home. For many dominants and slaves, this will be the extent of their interaction. For those people who live in areas with an active BDSM community, or who have like-minded friends, public service and play can form a large part of their relationship.

Escorting

A dominant may require her slave to escort her to various social functions, such as parties, theater performances, and the like. These situations give the slave a chance to perfect and display her social graces and poise. Public attendance can be extraordinarily challenging, especially for submissives who are accustomed to private service. The noise and bustle, the numerous chance encounters with strangers and friends, and the simple desire to do well can overwhelm a slave. Dominants should take time to acknowledge the slave's performance, either during or after the event.

Here a note on discretion is in order. There are relatively few public situations in which a dominant and slave can appear as they are – as owner and property. While Miss Abernathy believes that pride and confidence in one's life choices are laudable, she nevertheless cautions against inappropriate displays that may lead to conflict and confrontation. Taking your slave to The Four Seasons on a leash is not recommended. Neither is requiring obviously submissive behavior in front of a slave's professional colleagues, if such behavior would damage her credibility. Parents may still have their children removed from their care if their BDSM lifestyle becomes public. How much is public display worth to you?

Lending Slaves Out

If a dominant and his slave are part of the larger BDSM community in their area, they may wish to open their relationship to friends and other players. Very often this will take the form of lending the slave out. The slave may be sent to another top for discipline or to perform some special service, or may be engaged to help train a less experienced submissive in what may be called a "middle" position. If the slave has abduction or "gang" fantasies, the dominant may wish to arrange a group scene as a special treat. The dominant should take special care to inform the other players of the slave's interests and limitations and should observe the entire procedure carefully to ensure the slave's safety.

A special case is the slave auction. Most major American cities have social clubs and events for BDSM aficionados, where dominants and submissives can be open about their relationships and tastes. One favored event is the slave auction. Here a slave (or an unattached submissive) is put on the block and "sold" to the highest bidder. Often what is being auctioned is not the slave *in toto*, but "first negotiation rights" or a specific skill of the slave's, such as boot polishing or massage or cooking.

Group scenes do bring up the matter of jealousy, and it would be unwise to ignore it. Dominant/submissive relationships are by definition possessive, and it is not uncommon for a dominant to resent the attention his slave pays to another dominant (even if it has been negotiated) or for a slave to feel wounded at the sight of "her" dominant with another slave. Miss Abernathy's advice is "Know thyself." If you are a naturally jealous person, admit it. If you prefer a monogamous relationship, do not settle for anything else; you will only be miserable. There are dominants who find the idea of their slave serving anyone else appalling; there are certainly slaves who are happiest when focused on one person and one person only. Nowhere does it say that all BDSM players must be non-monogamous, although many are happily (and ethically) so. Choosing this lifestyle means choosing to live as you see fit, regardless of society's qualms. Do not then fall prey to another set of arbitrary rules.

Tools and Accoutrements for Training

Clothing

The clothing a dominant chooses for a slave should suit both the dominant's personal tastes and the practical requirements of the slave's position. It is ridiculous to ask a butler to wear a maid's uniform (except as a form of humiliating punishment) or to require a sex slave to be bundled up from head to toe.

In general, there are two schools of slave couture. The first believes that slaves should be naked at all times. This option is most practical for slaves who serve exclusively in the dominant's home or at play parties and is especially appealing for sex slaves. A slave may perform many tasks around the home while naked and not suffer any ill effects. (Two tasks that should be avoided are cleaning with caustic chemicals and cooking.)

The second school holds that slaves ought to be outfitted with a uniform appropriate to their status. A sissy maid should never be without stockings and gaff (an undergarment used to conceal male genitalia); a butler, without a dark formal suit. Sex slaves can also be outfitted in appealing lingerie or scanty skirts or loincloths that leave them physically accessible to the dominant at all times. Any slave who is engaged for sexual service should be prepared to strip down on command.

It is vital that the dominant provide adequate clothing for specific tasks. A slave who gardens should be given gloves and knee pads as well as the necessary tools for her work. If the slave has particularly sensitive skin, she should be given lined rubber gloves before being asked to wash dishes or scrub the toilet. It is appropriate, as part of the slave's training, to require a list of all the necessary "tools of the trade" for any given role or task. It is the dominant's responsibility to provide these items, unless other arrangements have been made.

Many slaves find that costumes or uniforms or the experience of forced nakedness trigger their submission. Likewise, dominants may find that certain articles of clothing – boots, a corset, a leather vest – put them in a more dominant frame of mind... and excite the submissive. If the slave has a fetish, the dominant may wish to indulge that fetish, or she may wish to save it for a special reward. Although a slave should be ready and willing to serve a Mistress who is wearing tennis shoes and sweatpants, both parties may want to experiment with costuming as an added perk.

Hidden Items

Many slaves benefit from the judicious use of "hidden" training devices that can be worn under street clothes. The transvestite maid who spends his days in an office may find the caress of a pair of silky panties or fine nylon stockings under his suit just the thing to help him through the day and prepare him for his evening chores. Sissy maids may be required to wear a gaff to disguise the male genitals, and a dominant may wish a slave to wear it on a daily basis. This form of training is especially efficacious if the maid is required to shop for the items himself, in, say, an exclusive boutique or at Victoria's Secret.

A dominant may also require the slave to wear a corset or waist-training belt under her work clothes. It is imperative that such items not restrict the slave's movement or respiration so severely as to interfere with her work or her health. A hidden item should be a constant, gentle reminder of the dominant and of the slave's status.

Some dominants favor the use of anal insertion devices ("butt plugs") in their training programs. Butt plugs, which are available in a wide variety of shapes, materials and sizes, are particularly beneficial for sex slaves of anally inclined masters and mistresses. They may also be used a punishment, although again, they should not interfere with the slave's ability to function in the workplace and should not damage his body. Therefore, plugs should not be left in place for more than a few minutes to start. The time may be increased to several hours as the slave adjusts. The anus can be stretched with increasingly large butt plugs, so that it may later accommodate other items, like a large penis, a latex-sheathed whip handle, or several gloved fingers.

Female slaves whose masters wish to train them for more active sexual service may wish them to "pack" – that is, to wear a strap-on dildo under their regular clothing. This technique is also useful for gender-switching women who serve as "boys." There exists an under-ground literature – these days transmitted by way of the Internet – on the fine art of packing. Dildos, like butt plugs, come in a variety of shapes, sizes and materials, from soft "herbies" (sometimes called

"pants-fillers") to superhuman dongs. The slave can stuff a small, soft
dildo in her underwear – men's Y-fronts or a jockstrap are appropriate
choices – or can use a harness with larger toys. Harnesses are usually
made either of durable but soft leather, or of webbing. The former
has the benefit of high fetish value; the latter is easier to clean, lighter
in weight, and less expensive. The slave should be instructed in the
proper care of both dildo and harness and should learn the advantages
of different styles of underwear and trousers, the merits of condoms
(and their use) and the most pleasing way to handle "her dick."
Pornography featuring male-male scenes may form an important part
of her education.

S/M Tools

Not all submissives are masochists and not all dominants are
sadists. In the event that this happy convergence of tastes occurs,
however, the dominant may wish to acquire and use tools designed
for S/M play. Physical sensation can be used as a punishment or as a
reward. Choose your "weapon" well: trainers may prefer a leather
strap, while a governess may reach for a fine rattan cane. A canine
trainer may prefer a rolled-up newspaper; the equestrienne, a crop.
Or the dominant may choose to make her open hand a tool: a firm
swat on the behind makes a fine choice as reward or punishment.

PART TWO:
D/S RELATIONSHIPS

*In which we explore the nature and logistics of
dominant/submissive arrangements, from the
acquisition of slaves to the negotiation of contracts.*

Perhaps you are a dominant looking for a slave. How on earth
do you find one? You could look to that capricious mistress, Fate, to
deliver your future property to your doorstep, but burnt offerings or
no, the Goddess has a backlog of requests for happiness, so you
would do well to consider more mundane options.

Many people have successfully found partners through personal
ads in their local alternative papers or BDSM contact magazines like
Bitches With Whips, Kinky People, Places and Things, Tough Customers,
or the *Sandmutopian Guardian*. Computer bulletin boards also
provide a source of potential partners. A number of excellent books
can give you tips on finding partners (see the resource guide for
suggestions). In addition to advertising and "cruising" the Internet,
many dominants and submissives enjoy the support and stimulation
of BDSM organizations. Most major American cities boast several
such organizations; some, like New York's Eulenspiegel Society and

San Francisco's Society of Janus and Outcasts, have existed for many years. Most organizations offer educational workshops and social events for their membership; some host BDSM play parties; many publish newsletters. The Eulenspiegel Society's quarterly newsletter, *Prometheus*, is available to non-members and features well-written articles and beautiful graphics along with event listings and advertising. Joining one of these organizations and attending BDSM parties, conferences, contests, and events are certainly the most direct methods of meeting compatible individuals.

How do you signal your interest in D/S? The lesbian and gay leather communities have their hanky codes: a bandanna displayed on the left by tops, on the right by bottoms, with every color of the rainbow signifying a particular activity or fetish. I have yet to see a hanky that signified dominance or submission, however, although some, like white lace for Victorian scenes, can be adapted for that use. Other writers and craftspeople have suggested rings (such as the Gauntlet piercing studio's reproduction of the ring worn by the dominants in *Story of O*), bracelets or anklets, or other trinkets.

My suggestion is this: wear whatever suits you and let your manner speak for you. By this I do not mean that dominants should be indiscriminately haughty; this is rudeness, not dominance. Nor do I advise submissives to throw themselves willy-nilly at the feet of dominants. Such behavior is disrespectful, both to the dominant and to the submissive himself. An attitude of quiet, attentive grace suits a submissive better than wanton gestures of abasement. Likewise, an observant and controlled manner conveys dominance more readily than pushiness or obnoxious, egocentric displays of "power."

What To Look For In a Submissive

Beyond mere availability and erotic compatibility, what qualities should a dominant look for in a potential slave? Here Miss

Abernathy must admit to a certain prejudice. For many dominants, the intellectual acumen of a slave and his or her spiritual development are relatively unimportant. Not so for me. I am simply uninterested in a slave with whom I cannot carry on a lively conversation. In fact, my personal list of required qualities begins with "highly verbal." Clearly, certain roles require specific skills: it would be foolish to employ a cook who burns water. Half the pleasure of owning a slave is in the training, however – so if what you want is only a cook, call an agency and hire a cook. If what you want is an accomplished chef who has a foot fetish or who can recite Yeats while being caned or who is willing and able to learn French so that she can accompany you to the film festival at Cannes, that is a slave.

In general, though, I believe that all slaves should exhibit some basic qualities. A slave should be sincere, loyal, discreet, clean, modest, honest, graceful, intelligent (that is, able to learn what is required for her position), respectful of herself and others, observant, attentive, and ethical.

In addition to these basic qualities, a dominant may require other characteristics, such as physical attractiveness, strength or stamina, specific sexual traits, a pleasant voice (particularly important for slaves to be voice-trained), social adaptability, or specific technical skills (construction, sewing, writing, accounting and the like).

I would like to say a word about a particular phenomenon that may arise between submissive and dominant. You will remember, no doubt, the urgency with which Severin pursued his Mistress, Wanda, in *Venus In Furs*. What you may not recall is her initial reluctance to fulfill his fantasy. It is possible to read *Venus In Furs* as the story of a would-be slave who is submissive only to his own fantasies. Gregor (as Severin was called while in service to his lady) is a textbook example of a pushy submissive who "tops from the bottom." I do not wish to imply that a real-life submissive should have no input into a contract or the ways in which it is carried out, but there is a qualitative difference between a dominant who enters into a contract freely – who indeed will most often initiate it – and one who is bullied into adopting a "dominant" position by a needy submissive. Gregor created a monster in Wanda, one with whom he quickly became dissatisfied. I refer to the tendency to bully people into dominance as "Gregor Syndrome"; individuals afflicted with it should be avoided.

To Those Who Would Be Masters...

Personal Qualities of a Good Dominant

Just as a slave must exhibit exemplary qualities, so must a dominant show that he is worthy of the privilege of ownership. Just because a person is a sexual "top" or sadist does not automatically mean that he will be a good dominant.

First and foremost, the dominant should possess at least the same level of personal integrity that he expects from his slave. While "do as I say, not as I do" may be an amusing erotic game, it cannot, in the long run, form the basis of a dominant/submissive arrangement.

Second, the dominant should have a clear sense of his own limitations and needs, and be able to articulate them clearly and succinctly. A dominant must have exceptionally good personal boundaries, particularly since slavehood implies a level of dependence on the dominant.

Third, a dominant should be inquisitive. The best dominants are insatiably curious about human nature. This curiosity drives such individuals to dig deep into the hearts and minds of submissives to discover what makes them tick. A dominant must be highly observant – nosy, even. Selective prying is the dominant's prerogative.

A dominant should be creative, versatile, and decisive, both in matters of reward and of punishment. The tasks she sets for her submissive, the authority with which she presents new restraints and challenges, the ingenuity with which she approaches the training process – all these are vital if the dominant wishes to avoid boredom and conventionality in her relationships.

I believe that a dominant should herself have an intimate knowledge of the tasks she sets for a submissive. So, while she need not be physically able to do a task herself, she should both understand the logistics of the problem and appreciate the skill and energy necessary to complete it. Not only does this assure that the dominant will value the slave appropriately, but it will also allow her to the better correct the slave in the event of an error or insufficiency in the work. A dominant must be both teacher and student, able to learn from her peers – and from her slaves.

This raises the broader question of nature versus nurture. Are the best dominants born, or are they made? Old School wisdom has it that the best tops start at the bottom; that is, that a would-be dominant should undergo training as a submissive in order to appreciate the complexities of service. To the extent that this is possible, given the resources of the community and the individual's temperament, I think it is sound advice. Certainly there are those who are constitutionally unsuited for submission, and I am not suggesting that such individuals force themselves into an unnatural role. To them I recommend extensive observation of successful D/S relationships, and, if possible, the experience of co-topping or co-owning a submissive. Indeed, some of the most successful masters have been trained by slaves or by more experienced dominants in exactly this manner.

Just as submissives can suffer from "Gregor Syndrome," dominants are prone to a number of ailments as well. The most general is known as "top's disease," or, in common parlance, delusions of grandeur. Just because you are suzy slave's master doesn't mean you are automatically Master of the Universe. It is inappropriate and downright rude to try to dominate innocent bystanders; in some cases, this behavior can become abusive.

A related ailment is "Wanda Syndrome," named after Gregor's mistress in *Venus In Furs*. A dominant suffering from Wanda Syndrome is actually letting herself be dominated by her so-called submissive. Often this leads to resentment, and, in some cases, betrayal and abandonment, as was the case in Sacher-Masoch's novel. Passive-aggressive behavior and codependency are as unhealthy in a dominant/submissive relationship as in any other.

Commitment and Resources

Just as slavehood can be a vocation, responsible and committed dominance can be a source of great joy and satisfaction. However, in the desire to possess and care for a submissive, some dominants overestimate their own level of commitment and resources. If you are having trouble paying your own rent, it is foolish to take on a live-in slave. If you are a naturally monogamous person, contracting with a submissive whose greatest fantasy is to be lent out to your friends would be a grave error.

One dominant of my acquaintance has written, "The Mistress must be worthy of the servant." I can only applaud her. I believe that the best dominants are essentially modest. A modest dominant is not an oxymoron. She must know her limits and her weaknesses as well as her strong points; how else can she dare to correct someone else's? She does not suffer from delusions of grandeur or overestimate her abilities. She does not believe herself to be a panacea for the world's ills, and especially not for a submissive's inner pain. No one, but no one, can "cure" another person's childhood wounds or spiritual malaise. At best, a dominant can help create a supportive atmosphere in which to allow a submissive to heal those wounds herself.

Styles of Dominance

Just as there is a wide variety of submissives, dominants do not come in one flavor only. There are the classic roles of *mistress* and *master*. (It should be noted that masters may be female or male. Some women prefer the title *mastress*. I suppose that there may also be male mistresses, although I do not know any personally.) The archetypal mistress is a leather goddess wearing towering spike-heeled boots; she is wasp-waisted in her corset and brandishes a whip. Yet how many women are inclined to prance around their homes in clothing that is more like bondage than any chains? Very few, in my experience. More often, "mistress" is a general title of respect for a dominant woman, whatever her style. Likewise, a master may be macho in his chaps and mirrored shades – or a friendly gentleman in a business suit. *Nota bene:* just as a submissive may well be offended by a random individual trying to "top" her, many dominants dislike being addressed as "master" or "mistress" without prior negotiation, even in a kink-friendly environment.

The key aspect of a mistress or master is authority, and especially authority based on personal achievement. We speak of a master craftsperson or of a Master of Arts degree. In both of these cases, the title of "master" is conferred after years of training and work. Likewise in D/S, the title of master or mistress ought to be earned, not taken.

Another role is that of the *trainer*. Trainers often model themselves after athletic, military, or animal trainers; they are often primarily concerned with performance. The trainer is the natural complement to the pet; a *butler* in the middle position of supervising other slaves may also act as a trainer.

An *owner* can be a master, trainer, or mistress; here the emphasis is on the submissive as possession. Owners are suitable dominants for pets and for slaves who enjoy being first and foremost someone's property.

A final category of dominant is the ***teacher.*** In this group we find governesses, headmasters and -mistresses, the Mother Superior and the local priest. In all cases, the dominant stands *in loco parentis,* assuming a disciplinary pseudo-parental role. A teacher may also take on a dominant-in-training. In any case, one would expect a teacher to have a particular area of expertise, be it French or fencing.

To Those Who Would Be Slaves...

While this book is primarily addressed to dominants, I have no doubt that some submissives will have braved their way through it as well. If you are one of these, you are to be commended...but also forewarned. It takes more than good posture and pretty manners to make a slave. I must repeat myself: slavehood is a vocation. It requires patience, hard work, unflinching honesty, and a strong sense of self. The following short essay will, I trust, give you food for thought on your journey.

On Ethics

Miss Abernathy strongly believes that our world and our community cries out for a more balanced and harmonious ethical structure, one that ends neither in an eye-for-an-eye literalism nor in a turn-the-other-cheek denial of the self. I find in medieval chivalry an embodiment of such a system. The following pages do not contain a lengthy discussion of chivalry as a historical and literary phenomenon. Rather, I have taken the terminology of chivalric ethics as a starting point for a discussion of submission and service.

While this section is addressed primarily to submissives, I hope it will become apparent that these guidelines represent an ethical structure appropriate to dominants as well.

Foundations of Submissive Ethics

In his romance Lancelot (The Knight of the Cart), the twelfth-century French poet Chrétien de Troyes tells the story of a famous knight in service to a famous queen. Lancelot has vowed to do his lady's will without hesitation, thinking not of himself, but only of her wishes. One day, the queen requires Lancelot to climb into a cart — which, the author tells us, was used in those times like a pillory, to display common criminals to public mockery. The proud knight, forgetting his vow, hesitates for the space of two steps, and the queen rebukes him, causing him no end of distress. When the two finally meet again, he asks why she has ignored him, her faithful lover.

Then the queen explains to him:

> *"What? Were you not then ashamed and afraid of the cart? You showed great reluctance to climb in when you hesitated for the space of two steps. That indeed was why I refused either to address you or to look at you." "May God save me," says Lancelot, "from doing such a wrong a second time; and may God never have mercy on me if you were not absolutely right! [...]."* (trans. D.D.R. Owen)

What kind of a relationship is this, where one partner may ask the other to humiliate himself publicly for her sake? Courtly love, although it is the source of many of our modern notions of romantic love, diverges sharply from its contemporary counterpart in that love is explicitly defined in terms of the lover's service to his lady. The relationship is one of fealty, a vow of devotion to an individual and commitment to serving him or her. Such was a knight's vow to his king, and such is that same knight's vow to his lady love.

The unattainable woman. The devoted lover. Seemingly random acts of disdain that humiliate the lover. His continued adoration and increased fervor. We might just as easily be reading Sacher-Masoch's *Venus In Furs* as a medieval romance. Just as Gregor submits to the humiliation of traveling as Wanda's servant, riding in crowded, smelly coaches with the commoners and sleeping in cold and drafty servant's quarters, Lancelot, the flower of chivalry, submits to the punishment of the cart: the mark of the common, the mean. And all for love.

What qualities did a chivalrous lover possess? What did he offer his lady in return for her affection? And how can a modern submissive interpret and adapt this seemingly archaic system to his own situation? What does it really mean to love, honor, and obey?

Friendship

I believe that no dominant/submissive relationship can exist without the bonds of mutual affection. I am not talking about a casual affair or mere erotic titillation, but about an ongoing committed relationship. Love and acceptance are the basis of such a union. A submissive should be first and foremost a trusted companion to the dominant. Obedience, which often stands firmly at the center of any spoken or written contract between a dominant and a submissive, grows out of the trust established by love.

Honor

While friendship and obedience develop between two people, honor is a matter of individual discretion and conscience. Honor is both a personal quality and a system of values according to which we make decisions. It is based on discernment, a realistic sense of order and fairness. There was a time when an honorable woman would not dream of "compromising herself" with pre- or extra-marital sex; for some people, this rule still holds true. A man of honor would not let a slanderous remark against himself or his family go unavenged. For the purposes of a submissive ethic, honor is an internal sense, one which allows the individual to make judgments about a given person, action, or situation. In the most general terms, "being honorable" is an old-fashioned way of saying that an individual has appropriate and consistent boundaries, that she is able to say, "This is acceptable; that, however, is not." It is vital for a submissive to be able to articulate her sense of honor, both in negotiation and in service.

"No, I refuse to speak badly of the Mistress in public." "No, I cannot serve you in any way that endangers my ability to earn a living or that compromises my physical and emotional safety." "No, I will not engage in behavior that my Owner has forbidden me, even though I know he'll never find out."

Truthfulness

A prerequisite to honor is truthfulness. Truthfulness is the ability to be honest with oneself and with others about one's feelings and motivations and to communicate these as accurately as possible. This quality includes the ability to say, "I don't know how I feel about that yet. Please give me some time to think about it," or "My feelings about that have changed. Here's where I stand now." If a submissive is not truthful, she cannot give informed consent, or more accurately, the dominant cannot be held responsible if, after complying with the submissive's expressed desires, the submissive complains. If she communicates a change in her feelings or perceptions – "I thought I'd like being put in a cage and ignored, but I found out I hated it" – that is one thing. That is being truthful. But complaints such as "You should have known not to call me a slut!" when no such boundary had been communicated are unacceptable. Any sentence that begins with "you should have known" indicates a lack of communication or of truthfulness.

Humility

Humility, like modesty, has an undeserved bad reputation. By humility I do not mean rampant self-deprecation or -hatred. I do mean a realistic perception of one's abilities and desires. This includes the ability to say to oneself and others, "I was wrong," or "I made a mistake," or "I misjudged my ability to do that for you." Likewise, a humble person will accept constructive criticism eagerly, finding in it the nugget of truth that is the key to self-betterment. Often our desire to please is so great that we undertake tasks for which we are not sufficiently prepared. There is nothing dishonorable about striving for a goal; what is dishonorable is the refusal to admit not being able to achieve that goal right now.

Accomplishment

Submissives, like knights, need to acquire special skills. A lady's maid will need extensive knowledge of make-up techniques and grooming, while a cook may want to attend a culinary school. The most famous courtly lover, Tristan, spoke many languages, played several instruments, was adept at hunting and dressing game, was an excellent fighter and statesman, and played a mean game of chess to boot. Self-betterment in one's chosen arts befits a submissive as well as it does a chivalrous knight.

Courtesy

We speak of the uncommon quality of common courtesy. Courtesy is, at base, a matter of respect. If we respect another person's time, personal space, and rights, then we will naturally act in a way that expresses that respect. If we respect their time, we will not arrive late to appointments. If we respect their personal space, we will not scatter our things around their home nor will we touch the person without invitation. We will allow them privacy. If we respect their rights, we will allow them to say "no" to us, to maintain their property, and to make decisions regarding their own health and welfare.

One must also be willing to extend such courtesy to oneself. We must, in all humility, respect our own needs for food, rest, privacy, recreation and the like. It is a discourtesy to others to be discourteous to oneself, in that denying our own human needs makes us all the more likely to disappoint our friend by being incapable or exhausted or otherwise unprepared for service.

Fidelity

Fidelity is a much-neglected virtue among submissives. As a group, submissives are infected with a scarcity mentality, which tells them that there are far too many bottoms and far too few tops. They feel this gives them permission to speak badly of a former partner in hopes of winning a new one, or to act as if a friend is only a friend as long as he does not stand in the way of a relationship with a desirable dominant. Yet, an honorable submissive can only gain from a refusal to compromise existing, valued friendships.

Goodness (Integrity)

Integrity implies probity, a view of the self as a rounded and consistent whole. When a submissive strives to be "good," he is striving after integrity, the sense of security that comes from living in right relation to himself, the dominant, and the world.

The essence of goodness, of personal integrity, is compassion, a willingness to look into one's own heart and the hearts of others and be witness to human suffering. A compassionate submissive is one who will look beyond his own good and that of his master, to the greater goods of family and community. A slave's acts of kindness reflect upon the dominant as well as upon the slave himself. The willingness to undertake an action simply because it is right marks a submissive as superior; indeed, he may be on the road to perfection.

Support for Submissives

As blissful as slavehood may be for those called to it, submissives run the risk of extreme isolation. It is vital that slaves maintain friendships outside of their dominant/submissive relationship, particularly with other slaves. Dominants should encourage such friendships, and any person who isolates a submissive from all other human contact is not dominant, but misguided. I encourage you to seek out BDSM organizations and publications that portray slavehood positively. Some of these organizations and publications are listed in the resource guide at the end of this book.

Taxonomy of Slavehood

The roles a submissive may play in the life of a dominant are as varied as that dominant's needs and her submissive's desires and skills. While many people envision slavehood according to the *Story of O* model, for a some submissives, genital sex is of secondary or even negligible importance. Such submissives find true satisfaction in the simple act of service and are therefore known as service-oriented submissives. What type of services can a submissive provide? Any and all!

Houseslaves

Imagine yourself in the home of a wealthy nineteenth century British family. If you've seen reruns of "Upstairs, Downstairs" or "Brideshead Revisited" on PBS, you'll know exactly what I'm referring to – the place is crawling with servants.

When you arrived at your friends' home, you might first be met by a *footman* who would help you out of your carriage or, if you arrived on horseback, would see that your steed was taken safely to the stables. (The modern equivalent, of course, is the *chauffeur*.) At the door, the *butler* would greet you. The role of the butler – or in exceptionally wealthy households, the *steward* – is as the dignified head of the serving hordes. He – though in our day and age, a female butler is perfectly acceptable – sees to it that the household runs smoothly, that servants are generally neither seen nor heard, and that guests and family members are attended to. In general, he answers to no one but the master or mistress of the house. (You may have noticed that in novels butlers are often called by their last names; in the nineteenth century, this was a mark of rank in service.) The butler often occupies a "middle" position – he is subordinate to his employers, but in charge of all the other servants. A dominant who has a number of slaves may elect a more experienced submissive to act as a butler or major domo in supervising the other slaves. The primary qualities of a good butler are loyalty and a strong sense of decorum. Submissives who feel called to the role of butler are often fastidious and detail-oriented and are comfortable juggling many tasks at once. They are the image of grace under pressure.

Both women and men may act very well as *maids*. (The special case of the transvestite or "sissy maid" will be discussed below.) Maids' duties include all aspects of household maintenance, such as cleaning, laundry, shopping, and other errands. In some cases, an experienced maid, the *housekeeper,* may also supervise other servants. Some maids may serve in the kitchen, or a dominant may make use of a cook. If the dominant is so inclined, maids can be trained in special sorts of service, as, for example, tea service or serving at formal dinner parties. Older editions of etiquette manuals can provide a wealth of useful information for luncheon, tea, and dinner service for maids of more traditionally minded dominants.

Similar to the maid is the *houseboy.* This term is used for a servant of general usefulness who may do all that maids do in the home, but who is often employed at odd jobs – gardening, driving, carpentry and the like – in accordance with his training.

Related to the butler is the *valet.* Generally thought of in service to a dominant man, the valet acts as personal assistant in dressing and grooming. In certain periods, the valet was simply referred to as the master's "man." (Readers familiar with Dorothy Sayers's Lord Peter Wimsey mysteries will no doubt remember the inimitable Bunter.) The valet may also act in his master's stead, delivering messages, arranging schedules, and generally acting as a guy/gal friday.

The feminine (although not necessarily female!) counterpart to the valet is the *lady's maid*. Just as the valet is concerned with the master's wardrobe, so the lady's maid acts as hair stylist, costume consultant, and general companion to a dominant woman. A lady's maid is often on more intimate terms with her mistress, acting as confidante and counselor. In the nineteenth century, the lady's maid was given her mistress's old dresses and sewing scraps to keep or to sell.

Such are the traditional appointments for household servants.

Sex Slaves

Many submissives' fantasies contain a distinctly erotic tone; indeed, most people engage in D/S play for the simple reason that it excites them. (And, in fact, no other reason is needed!) For some submissives, sexual servitude lies at the center of their eroto-emotional life. These submissives are best suited to be *sex slaves* or *sex toys*. In such arrangements, the sex slave exists for no other reason than the physical pleasure of the dominant. Often the slave's dress – or lack of it – will be designed to enhance her availability. While at the Chateau, O and her fellow slaves were required to wear elaborate dresses that exposed their breasts and genitals to all the company. When in the mundane world, René required O to go without panties, to seat herself with her bare rump flush against the seat, to keep her lips slightly parted to suggest openness to invasion, to wear blouses that allowed him access to her nipples, and so on. And just as O was initiated into anal sex by Sir Stephen, sex slaves should be trained in the specific sexual arts that please the dominant.

Of course, a slave of any type may also be used as a sex slave, if that is his desire and that of the dominant.

Cross-Dressers

I have mentioned the *sissy maid* or panty slave. The subject of a whole sub-genre of erotic literature, the sissy maid is generally a man whose fantasy is to serve a lady while he is cross-dressed. The cross-dressing may be hidden (when the dominant orders the man to wear women's panties or stockings under his clothes) or transformational. In the latter case, the submissive strives to look as feminine as possible. He may wear a "gaff," a garment designed to hold the penis and testicles tucked under the body to give the illusion of a feminine shape under panties. Sissy maids are often employed for formal affairs or tea service. They may eroticize service in and of itself, or they may desire to be the object of the company's attention. Elaborate maid's costumes are available for these submissives, and the outfits range from the traditional short-skirted black and white dress to downright tarty red affairs.

Slave Without a Master: Ronin

What about a person who feels called to slavehood and yet has no master or who has lost his master? Such a submissive is sometimes called "ronin," the name for a "rogue" samurai warrior. Submissives can certainly undertake general training by themselves; many of the techniques I discuss here can be adapted to create an individual training program. If slavehood is indeed your calling, patience is in order. Cultivate yourself as if you were already serving your ideal master. There is no more effective way to attract him.

Types of Arrangements: The D/S Relationship

Perhaps you have examined yourself closely, and know who you are and what you want. Perhaps you have even found the slave of your dreams. Now what? How do you make those dreams come true in our waking reality?

Starting Slow: The Part-Time D/S Relationship

I believe the phrase "casual dominant/submissive relationship" to be a contradiction in terms. I hold that effective and satisfying D/S relationships depend on genuine affection and intimacy between the partners, and affection and intimacy do not develop during a ten-minute negotiation at an S/M play party. Certainly dominant and submissive elements are an integral part of many S/M scenes, but the sort of service-oriented submission that I am discussing here does not lend itself to casual encounters.

This does not mean, however, that short-term or occasional D/S arrangements do not exist; in fact, they are quite common. The slave who cleans his Mistress's house once a month; the submissive carpenter who builds bondage equipment for her dominatrix friend in exchange for a session; two men who live 3,000 miles away from each other and negotiate a weekend-long contract once a year: all of these can be considered "casual," and yet clearly dominant/submissive, relationships. Indeed, many regular clients of professional dominants fall into this category. Over time, trust and a certain level of intimacy develop between client and dominant, and lifestyle dominants take the training of a sincere client very seriously. Acquaintances that begin as "casual" or occasional may well develop into long-term relationships.

Telephone, Computer, and Postal Training

In our jet-set world, it is often impossible for a dominant and her slave to spend as much time together as they like. Even live-in slaves must sometimes be separated from their owners by business trips and family obligations. Luckily, it is not difficult to maintain contact across the miles.

Many professional dominants begin training potential clients by mail. The prospective client is expected to show proper respect and follow directions. The training may be as simple as returning a questionnaire or answering a letter, or it may require that the submissive assume a specific posture (kneeling, for example) while writing to the dominant, wear certain articles of clothing (panties, a cock ring), use special written forms of address, and send photos to prove that he has done his part. This sort of training can be adopted by other dominants as well. It is a wonderful option for individuals whose partners live at a distance or who travel a great deal.

A related form of training is by electronic mail. "Cyberslaves" have the advantage of instant contact with the dominant. There is some concern among Internet users that online exchanges may not be as private as we might hope. Anonymous fileservers do exist, and are one option to explore if privacy is an issue. The same techniques used in postal training are appropriate for e-mail, but the dominant should remember to leave the slave's hands – at least one of them! – unoccupied so that she can type.

There is an entire industry devoted to sexual encounters by phone, and people are often surprised to learn how many phone sex customers are looking for a dominant. Phone training demands a vivid imagination and some acting skill, but it has the added appeal of instant feedback – you can hear the passion and desire in a slave's voice, the demanding presence of the dominant in his speech. BDSM "party lines" exist all over the country – check any mainstream pornographic magazine – although callers should take care not to give out too much information to strangers (home addresses, for example). Many professional dominants will do sessions by phone as well.

"Please, Sir, May I Have Some More?": Full-Time Relationships

Total Slavehood: Fact or Fiction?

Many readers of BDSM erotica develop a curious tendency to confuse fiction and reality. Let me reiterate: *Story of O* is a work of fiction. That is, it is an artfully told lie that manages nonetheless to tell us something of the truth. But that truth is not literal. Certainly dominants pierce and brand their slaves; some may even own villas on the outskirts of Paris. But I'm afraid I must disappoint you: excruci-atingly wealthy sadists with stables of nubile young women at their beck and call are not the norm. Such stories do express the depth of a submissive's desire, the passion a dominant feels at the willing submis-sion of a loved one, and the often mysterious workings of the erotic imagination. To the extent that they portray these emotions, the stories are true.

This is not to say that full-time slaves and their masters do not exist. It has become a commonplace in introductory BDSM litera-ture to pooh-pooh the concept of 24-hour-a-day, 7-day-a-week dominant/submissive relationships, and indeed, such correctives for the overactive imagination are necessary. Yet, to the extent that a slave arranges his life around his Master's and maintains constant awareness of his calling as a slave, I believe he embodies the ideal of the "total" slave. It is the ordering of one's life according to the principles of service that makes one a slave, not a collar or a contract or an afternoon workshop.

Live-Ins

A "live-in" is, as the term suggests, a slave who lives with his or her dominant. In our imaginations, the live-in has become the archetypal slave, waiting patiently in a corner, naked and collared, always at his Master's beck and call. But how can relatively average people live like this?

There are three models for a live-in relationship: marital, depen-dent, and employee. It is instructive to look at the ways in which these models, as economic contracts, allow for a division of labor and responsibility between two parties.

In the marital or partner model, one person or both parties may work to earn an income, as is now the case in many domestic part-nerships. In theory, the dominant gets to say how the money is spent, although in practice, this task is often delegated to the submissive. The submissive is expected to run the household, provide for the comfort of the dominant on a day-to-day basis, and in return, can expect security and affection.

In the dependent model, the submissive is treated as a financial dependent, like a child. Here the submissive is supported by the dominant, or, if the submissive earns an income, he turns it over to the dominant. In most cases, the dominant saves or invests that money to create a trust fund for the submissive. In return, the submissive is expected to perform certain chores or tasks in the household. The submissive may be given an allowance, but he remains essentially dependent on the dominant.

The third model is the employer-employee model. In this case, the submissive lives rather like an *au pair:* he receives room, board and a modest sum of money in return for specific tasks, be it chauffeuring or shopping.

In practice, relationships run according to these models may look alike, but the assumptions that underlie them are very different. The marital model is first and foremost a partnership, and for that reason it is the most workable model for most people who are not independently wealthy. The dependent model presupposes that the dominant has or makes enough money to support two people, or has enough financial savvy to invest the submissive's money wisely. The *au pair* model is appropriate for dominants who work at home and need a personal secretary, and for submissives with very specific, marketable talents. (My rule of thumb is, if the submissive would be paid for doing a task in the mundane world, she should receive equal recompense in some mutually agreeable form, be it legal tender, living space, or service trade.)

Contracts

Miss Abernathy is a great believer in contracts. There is a qualitative difference between saying "OK, you like canes, your safeword is 'mercy' and you hate gags. Got it!" and signing a piece of paper that specifies the rights and responsibilities of both parties. We live in a litigious culture, and contracts carry weight.

The basic purpose of a contract is to spell out, in as much detail as possible, the responsibilities of both parties, and the benefits they may expect.

The most notorious BDSM contracts are undoubtedly those that Leopold von Sacher-Masoch negotiated, on separate occasions, with his lovers, Fanny von Pistor and Wanda von Dunajew. Reprinted in Krafft-Ebing's famous work, *Psychopathia sexualis*, they are two very different examples of contracts between a dominant and submissive. In the first, limited contract, Sacher-Masoch agreed "on his word of honor, to be Frau von Pistor's slave, to fulfill her every wish and command for a period of six months." For her part, Frau von Pistor agreed not to demand anything "dishonorable of Sacher-Masoch (i.e. that would make him dishonorable as a person or a citizen)"; to allow him time to work each day; to give him complete privacy in his correspondence and other writings; to punish him for his offenses according to her judgment; to wear fur as often as possible, "and especially when she is cruel." The contract also provided for re-negotiation and for long periods of interruption, at Frau von Pistor's discretion. As it stands, this contract can be adapted to fit the needs of modern dominants and submissives.

The contract between Sacher-Masoch and Wanda von Dunajew is somewhat lengthier and of a very different bent. In it, Sacher-Masoch gives up the pretense of bourgeois respectability that he had with Frau von Pistor, and signs over his body and soul to Wanda, giving her permission to make him a criminal and to "martyr him with all the torments imaginable, even to death."

I hope it will be clear from the preceding discussion that the second contract is a work of the erotic imagination, and it is hardly surprising that Krafft-Ebing saw in Leopold von Sacher-Masoch a man obsessed. It should also be clear that neither of these contracts would hold up in a court of law.

An example of a more modern and realistic contract can be found in *The Lesbian S/M Safety Manual* (ed. Pat Califia). Written by Diane Vera, the contract provides for the dominant's "full owner-ship and use of [the submissive's] body and mind" for a specified period of time. The contract enumerates the slave's responsibilities in general terms: obedience; renunciation of personal pleasure, except as permitted by the dominant; truthfulness; acceptance of criticism and punishment; effort to act in accordance with the dominant's wishes in all things. Most important, though, the submissive accepts the dominant's will "[w]ithin the limits of physical safety and [the submissive's] ability to earn a livelihood." In her notes on the con-tract, Vera states, "Except in authoritarian religious cults, I doubt that anyone can totally surrender his/her autonomy forever, though doing so temporarily can be an exciting and emotionally rewarding experi-ence for some people."

Both Sacher-Masoch's and Vera's contracts are general; slave contracts can also be extraordinarily detailed. Clauses can and should include the following:

- safewords or some other signal for a "time-out"
- specific responsibilities of both parties, including financial ones
- circumstances under which the contract will become null and void
- any physical or psychological limitations of the parties who may and may not know about the contract, or read it
- any specific rituals or formulas or titles that play a role in the fulfillment of the contract
- a discussion of collars, tokens, and/or permanent marks

ଔ punishments and rewards

ଔ the beginning and ending dates of the contract

A preliminary contract should be negotiated for a short period of time only – a weekend, or perhaps two weeks – after which the contract should be re-negotiated and any changes made. Some dominants prefer month-to-month contracts; others opt for three- or six-month periods. People change more quickly than contracts, so it is inadvisable to sign a contract for more than a year at a time.

Sample Slave Contract

Obviously, the details of any contract would depend on the circumstances and wishes of the signers. The following is a rather extensive sample contract that may be amended for more general use.

Consensual Slave Contract

This document is intended to specify the responsibilities of Jane Doe (hereafter "the slave") and John Smith (hereafter "the Owner") as part of a consensual arrangement between them. This agreement is valid from midnight of January 1, 1996 through midnight of March 1, 1996. This contract is a private agreement between the parties and under no circumstances is it to be read by anyone other than the undersigned.

This contract will become null and void if any of the following circumstances should occur:

a) *either party becomes seriously ill, is hospitalized, or dies, or if*

b) *either party is required to attend to urgent family or business matters that will take him or her away from home for more than fourteen (14) days. In this event, the undersigned may agree to put the contract on temporary "time out," and agree to negotiate for its reinstatement at the earliest possible date.*

I, Jane Doe, being of sound mind and body, do hereby submit my will to that of the Owner, John Smith. I wish to be his personal servant and sex slave. I agree to fulfill, to the best of my ability, the following provisions.

1)   The slave is to devote herself, in mind and in body, to the desires of the Owner. She will obey him without question, knowing that he will never knowingly subject her to anything that will cause her physical or mental harm.

2)   The Owner agrees to attend to the physical, mental and emotional well-being of the slave. To enable him to do so, the slave will answer any question put to her as clearly and honestly as she is able.

3)   The slave also agrees to make daily entries in a slave journal. Entries should be at least one page in length and are to be made in the approved written format, that is, without use of the first person singular pronoun ("I" or "me") and any first person singular possessive forms ("my" or "mine"). In addition, all references to the slave are to be made in lower-case while all references to the Owner are to be capitalized. The journal is to be addressed to the Owner and will be read by him and him alone. Should this contract be dissolved, the slave will retain sole possession of the slave journal.

4)   The slave will strive to maintain her health and vitality to better serve the Owner. She agrees to inform the Owner of any physical discomfort, such as back or knee pain, that she may notice during the course of service. The Owner agrees to provide, at his expense, any medication necessary to treat conditions that result from service and to keep a supply of such medication at his home. The slave agrees to abstain from alcohol for 24 hours before any training session.

5)   The slave agrees to maintain personal cleanliness in a manner suitable for service. She will remove all body hair on a regular

basis and will rouge her nipples before each training session. When so ordered, she agrees to receive a cleansing enema from the Owner.

6) The slave agrees to wear whatever clothing the Owner may choose. This includes, but is not limited to, items of clothing (such as a corset) that the Owner may require her to wear under her street clothes.

7) The slave agrees to make her body available to the Owner whenever, wherever, and however he wishes. The Owner accepts full responsibility for the slave's safety, and agrees not to require unprotected sex from the slave.

8) The slave's training will include one formal S/M session per month. These sessions will always conclude with a formal caning. The slave acknowledges that these sessions may result in marks and agrees to inform the Owner if she expects to be in a circumstance (such as a doctor's visit or massage) where such marks might be a source of unwanted attention.

9) The slave acknowledges that the safeword is "Mercy." If she calls "Mercy," the Owner will immediately cease whatever activity is in progress. The slave will then be given sufficient opportunity to voice her concerns or make requests. The Owner will then, to the best of his ability and in full consideration of the slave's well-being, decide whether to proceed with the activity.

10) The Owner will furnish all tools and implements of correction, as well as safer sex supplies. The single exception to this clause is that the slave will be expected to provide the Owner with a cane, to be used on her only, at the beginning of the first formal S/M session. The slave will be expected to clean and maintain all tools, including this cane.

11) In accordance with the slave's previously stated limits, the Owner agrees not to use language that calls into question the slave's intelligence, nor will he use language, gestures, or scenarios that put the slave in the role of an animal.

12) Should she displease the Owner, the slave agrees to submit to whatever punishment the Owner may deem necessary. In accordance with the slave's previously stated limits, the Owner agrees not to use a belt as an implement of correction. Punishments will be for the betterment of the slave only and will not be undertaken in anger.

13) The Owner agrees to furnish the slave with a token which symbolizes his complete possession of the slave. This token will be suitable to wear in all circumstances, and the slave is expected to wear it at all times.

14) In addition to the token, the Owner will provide a collar which the slave is to wear while serving in the Owner's home and while at leather community events. The collar remains the property of the Owner and is a symbol of his responsibilities toward the slave.

15) The slave is to address the Owner as "Sir" or "Sir John" unless otherwise directed. The slave will speak to the Owner with respect. This respect should extend to speaking of the Owner as well.

16) The slave agrees to perform, to the best of her ability, whatever household tasks the Owner requires of her. These will routinely include, but are not limited to, the following: washing, drying, ironing, folding, and putting away the laundry; sweeping and/or vacuuming the floors; preparing three dinners and one brunch per week.

17) *While in the Owner's home, the slave must ask permission before using any furniture, using the toilet, or eating with utensils.*

18) *The slave will be expected to accompany the Owner to one leather community social event each month. She agrees to "attend" the Owner at these events and renounces the right to move freely while doing so.*

signed, this day _____, 19_____.

_____

Jane Doe, slave

_____

John Smith, Owner

Ending an Association: The Importance of Pre-nuptials

I believe that any contract between a dominant and a submissive – and any negotiation, for that matter – should include an explicit agreement about what will happen should the association not work out. I call these agreements "pre-nuptials." We all know about the "honeymoon" period when new lovers float about, four feet off the ground. Once they come back to earth, the view can be very different.

If the dominant is contracting for a live-in slave, the pre-nuptial clause(s) should include provisions ensuring the material and emotional care of the slave should the dominant dissolve the contract. Certainly any income that the dominant has controlled or saved for the slave should be returned immediately, with interest. Any personal items that belonged to the slave before the contract should also be returned. I also suggest that the slave be given the option of retaining any written work produced at the dominant's command, such as journals or essays, or at least copies of these.

But will the dominant be responsible for any or all of the slave's moving costs, which can include sizable security deposits and rental fees? What about household items or toys bought during the contract with both parties' money? Is it the slave's blender because she used it more, or the dominant's because he paid for it with his credit card? When a relationship is ending, the last thing anyone wants is more grief. Spell it out. I strongly suggest consulting an attorney for advice on pre-nuptial clauses before signing a live-in contract. You can always pretend you're actually getting married or establishing a domestic partnership, if discretion is an issue. At very least, look at some of the excellent do-it-yourself law books available from Nolo Press that show sample contracts and pre-nuptial agreements. Many books written for newlyweds include sections on finances and pre-nuptials. A contract between a dominant and a submissive is a commitment of no less importance or complexity than any other relationship, whether the State acknowledges it or not. Often mar-riage is the only comparable situation, and dominants and submis-sives would do well to learn where they can.

In more formal, traditional dominant/submissive relationships, the dominant will take the lead, and that includes the prerogative of ending the relationship. I do not wish to imply that a slave has no right to end a relationship or that they are a "bad" slave for doing so, simply that the dynamics of such relationships often leave more room for the dominant to initiate change. One well-known dominant woman of my acquaintance feels strongly that it is not just her prerogative, but her responsibility, to end a relationship that may be damaging to the submissive's self-esteem or general well-being, whether or not the submissive believes that to be the case. While this attitude may at first glance seem arrogant, it in fact speaks of a commitment to care for the submissive, and an understanding of the pitfalls of submission. This is not the same thing as Wanda Syndrome, and this dominant is hardly giving herself permission to throw a slave out on her ear. Rather, she takes responsibility for the slave's well-being.

A word to slaves: I have had the misfortune to know a number of submissives who seem to believe that the dissolution of a contract gives them license to behave badly. You will have realized by now that I view slavehood as a noble vocation, and I expect a slave to act no less honorably than a dominant in the event that a relationship ends. Here are a few simple guidelines, which I believe constitute the basis for good manners and a good reputation (and, should it not be clear from the discussion above, let me say that these principles apply no less to dominants than to submissives):

ॐ Return all of the dominant's property to her. This may include, but is not limited to, collars; tokens of ownership not explicitly given to the slave (name tags or other jewelry); house and car keys; any legal documents (although the slave should certainly retain a copy of the contract itself); credit cards or checks issued in the dominant's name; any items borrowed from the dominant, such as clothing, or borrowed in the dominant's name, such as rented video tapes, library books, and the like. Needless to say, any fees incurred due to the submissive's neglect to return borrowed items should be promptly paid by the submissive.

ॐ Refrain from denigrating the dominant to mutual friends or in public. Unless you feel strongly that the dominant is a genuine menace to public safety – in which case you might as well speak to the police as to your friends – spreading malicious gossip in the community will only damage your own reputation. I do not wish to imply that a slave should not seek solace from his friends, and it is likely that some of these friends will also be acquainted with the dominant. (Here is an important reason for a submissive to cultivate friendships outside the BDSM community and outside his D/S relationship.) Still, it is unfair to expect mutual friends to take your side, or to take sides at all. Be as respectful of the dominant's privacy as you would expect him to be of yours.

℘ Give yourself sufficient time to heal from any emotional wounds you may have suffered in the relationship. Do not jump into another D/S relationship too quickly. It will typically take anywhere from one year to three for a person to work through the pain of a failed relationship. Resist the urge to fall at the feet of the next dominant who waves a collar in your direction. By all means, go out, socialize, play if you will, but if you attempt another relationship too quickly, you are likely to deliver damaged goods to the new dominant and doing yourself a great disservice.

IN CONCLUSION

While it takes a great deal of forethought, hard work, and dedication to create and maintain a successful D/S arrangement, the benefits to both dominant and submissive are immeasurable. In conclusion, I would like to share with you, gentle reader, the story of a very happy slave.

We will call him G. At this writing, he lives in a major American city, across the street from his Master, a well-known figure in the local leather community. The Master is in a committed relationship with another young man, his "boy." G. shows incredible devotion to his Master. He has arranged his life so that he may be at his Master's disposal at any time of day or night. This has meant taking an apartment close to his Master's home and finding a job that would allow him to wear his collar – a solid length of chain with a heavy padlock – to work.

It is essential to G's submission that he be ever and always his Master's. I have seen him walking down the street. He is a tall man and carries himself with such reserved dignity that strangers passing him stop and follow him with questioning eyes as he proceeds down the block. He treats friend and stranger alike with respect and grace. It is not just that he knows that any flaw in his deportment will be reported to his Master by mutual friends, of whom they have a great many in the city. He simply wants nothing more than to be a tribute to his Master at all times. And is that not the root of submissive desire?

What I have presented here is one woman's view of the dominant/submissive lifestyle. As a subjective portrayal, it is necessarily limited. Miss Abernathy would be happy to hear of your experiences with dominant/submissive relationships, slave training, or erotic role-play. Kindly send me your comments in care of the publisher, marking your letter "Attn.: C. Abernathy" to ensure prompt forwarding.

APPENDIX A
The Erotic Imagination:
A D/S Reading List

Nothing has done more to propagate and perpetuate the dream of erotic slavehood than literature. Miss Abernathy has no objections to erotica; in fact, I encourage my submissives to read everything they can get their hands on. Erotic literature is a treasure-trove of fantasy material, and a surprising amount of it can be adapted to real life. I'd like to take a brief look at some of the literary sources of D/S fantasies and realities.

The Marquis de Sade

Le divin marquis gave his name to a "pathology" only recently removed from psychiatric literature as an illness: Sadism. Sade was a remarkable figure and well worth reading if only to explore the expressions of an obsessive, encyclopedic brain. *The Hundred and One Days of Sodom* is a literal catalog of pain and pleasure, and *Justine* and its companion novel, *Juliette*, provide the basis for much modern BDSM literature. Yet, most twentieth-century readers will be disappointed by Sade's work. Sade fancied himself a philosopher, and, when it would get him out of the Bastille, a revolutionary. Sade's slaves are invariably young, beautiful noble-things with exotic faux-antique names; the masters often old and repulsive clergymen and whores. But if you enjoy graphic depictions of coprophilia, copious buggery and religious blasphemy, you'll love Sade.

Leopold von Sacher-Masoch: Venus In Furs

More to the point is the work of Leopold von Sacher-Masoch, a nineteenth-century Austrian novelist. The author of *Venus In Furs*, Sacher-Masoch was notorious in his own time as a decadent and deviant soul. It is to him that we owe the D/S contract, the use of "slave names," the integration of fetish and D/S, the archetypal female-dominant/male-submissive relationship, and the term "masochism." In psychiatric literature, "masochism" refers to behavior and desires that we would call "submissive" today; modern BDSM players often use "masochist" specifically to refer to a person who finds erotic satisfaction in physical sensation ("pain"). The narrator of Venus, the nobleman Severin, desires nothing more than to play the role of servant to a beautiful woman, Wanda. And it is to him that we can attribute what I call "Gregor Syndrome," or topping from the bottom.

Pauline Réage: Story of O

In 1954, a novel appeared that was to change the face of erotic literature forever. It told the story of the erotic enslavement of a French fashion photographer known only as O. Taken by her lover, René, to a chateau on the outskirts of Paris, O is introduced to an exclusive society of dominant men and women and their female sex slaves. Slowly she becomes involved in the Chateau's society and comes to recognize herself as a slave.

Story of O was extremely controversial when it first appeared. The identity of the author remained a mystery for many years, although the book became an underground classic. Noted feminists on both sides of the Atlantic decried it as sexist propaganda, while other critics commented on its authentic portrayal of the obsessive quality of the erotic imagination.

O has come to typify the role of the sex slave: willing and available, suggestible and passionate. It also introduced the theme of erotic marking. At different points in the book, O receives labia piercings and a brand that mark her as a slave. In short, *Story of O* set the standard for male-dominant/female-submissive erotica.

Anne Rice: Exit to Eden and the Sleeping Beauty Trilogy

This prolific author may be most famous for her vampire books, but she also wrote a number of pseudonymous erotic novels with strong BDSM themes. *Exit To Eden* is set on an island resort for the rich and submissive. Dominant trainer Lisa finds her match in client Elliot. This rather serious novel was recently made into a comic film. Even more notorious than *Exit to Eden* is the Sleeping Beauty trilogy (*The Claiming of Sleeping Beauty, Beauty's Punishment,* and *Beauty's Release*). These erotic fairy tales recount the enslavement of the lovely princess Beauty and her subsequent adventures at the hands of a bevy of dominant noblefolk. The books feature many scenes of erotic domination, including human ponies and sexual torture devices.

John Preston: Mr. Benson

What *Story of O* did for the male-dominant/female-submissive erotic imagination, John Preston's *Mr. Benson* did for gay men. This story of a young man's initiation into the world of D/S originally appeared in serial form in *Drummer* magazine and made Preston the object of adulation. "I enjoyed writing *Mr. Benson,*" Preston explained in his essay, "Flesh and the Word: My Life with Pornography," "but I didn't write it with a serious intent, no matter how seriously people took it eventually."

In many ways, *Mr. Benson* parallels *Story of O.* The dominant is extraordinarily wealthy and very mysterious. What begins as mere sexual attraction, ends, for the submissive, in a complete change of lifestyle. Despite its sensationalistic climax – white slavery, indeed! – *Mr. Benson* is an undisputed classic of gay male BDSM erotica.

Pat Califia: Macho Sluts, Doc and Fluff, Melting Point

If John Preston brought gay D/S out of the closet, Pat Califia did the same for lesbians. A longtime leather community activist and educator, Califia has penned two short story collections, *Macho Sluts* and *Melting Point*; a novel, *Doc and Fluff*; an introduction to S/M play for couples, *Sensuous Magic*; a guide to lesbian sexuality, *Sapphistry*; and a collection of essays on sexual politics, *Public Sex*. She has also edited such groundbreaking anthologies as *Coming To Power* and *Doing It For Daddy*. Many of her stories explore sexual taboos – incest, vampiristic bloodlust, cross-orientation sex, rape, and addiction – with honesty and artistry. Her work is essential reading for anyone interested in BDSM.

Laura Antoniou: The Marketplace Trilogy

Among the recent additions to the literature of D/S is the Marketplace trilogy by Laura Antoniou. Written under the pseudonym "Sara Adamson," Antoniou's novels – *The Marketplace* (1993), *The Slave* (1994), and *The Trainer* (1995) – represent some of the finest BDSM erotica today. Antoniou imagines a "slave society," not wholly unlike Réage's Chateau or Rice's exotic-erotic island resort, but exposes the inner workings of that society.

> *"'Inspirations' isn't the word for my early reading in the subgenre of 'slave society' erotic fiction. Catalytic would be more correct. I read them all, and found that they all touched something inside of me, but didn't fully explore the questions I had, the fantasies I dreamed, the reality I was living. I kept asking, could people really withstand this kind of life? And if their eroticism led them that far, what if they didn't get what they imagined? How could the economics work, and how would these people think about their lives, and the lives that touched theirs?"* (From an interview with the author)

Unlike many lesser lights, Antoniou is a strong writer. Her books have engaging storylines, developed characters, and startlingly realistic descriptions of BDSM relationships. In addition to the Marketplace books, she has edited a number of anthologies, including *Leatherwomen, Leatherwomen II, By Her Subdued,* and *Some Women.*

Other Titles

There are many other special interest BDSM titles available. Unfortunately, many of them are poorly written; some are bowdlerized classics. Here are some further suggestions for your library.

The Pearl is a collection of Victorian erotic stories and poems, many of them containing scenes of "domestic discipline."

Harriet Marwood, Governess (Anon.) is classic Victoriana for those with a taste for the birch.

Miss High Heels will appeal to sissy maids and other cross-dressers.

The *Gor* novels, a science fiction series that now runs to many volumes, is set in a male-dominated society. If you can ignore the passages that tout male social supremacy, the novels can be quite enjoyable.

Artemis Oakgrove has written the *Throne* Trilogy, urban fantasies featuring a wealthy butch lesbian and her slaves.

David Aaron Clark, author of *The Marquis de Sade's Juliette: Vengeance on the Lord,* has shown himself to be a promising writer of BDSM novels.

Finally, many popular vampire novels derive their appeal from the dark eroticism of those creatures of the night.

APPENDIX B
PROFESSIONAL BDSM

In addition to erotic literature, the novice's most common introduction to the world of BDSM is professional domination. Professional domination presents the paradox so common in the sex industry: who is serving whom? Is the domina in charge, or is the paying customer? Is the service that a client provides any less "real" than that of a live-in slave? Does the Mistress take her clients seriously as submissives?

The answer is, it depends. Unfortunately, some of the women advertising services as dominatrices don't even know which end of the riding crop to hold. However, a number of cities boast excellent and dedicated women (and some men) who take their profession very seriously. If you are lucky enough to live in the San Francisco Bay Area, you can visit any number of experienced dominas whose collective expertise and sincerity is unparalleled anywhere in the world. I have a listed several women in the resource guide who offer educational sessions and/or counseling for novices and couples in addition to private sessions. If you are considering visiting a professional dominant, I recommend that you read an intelligent little booklet, "Selecting a Professional Dominatrix," available from Diversified Services of Brighton, MA. (See Resource Guide for contact information.) Also, issue #13 of the *Sandmutopian Guardian* contains two excellent articles on the professional scene by well-known and respected Bay Area sex educators.

APPENDIX C
RESOURCE GUIDE

Caveat emptor! This guide cannot pretend to be comprehensive, never mind exhaustive. For every book or organization listed, a dozen more exist. Although a listing here does not imply an official endorsement, I have opted to list many people and establishments personally known to me, to assure that resources given here are as reliable and reputable as possible. The guide is therefore weighted toward the San Francisco Bay Area with some listings from New York and the Boston area. No slight is intended to readers elsewhere. More extensive listings can be found in some of the introductory BDSM books, such as *SM 101* by Jay Wiseman and *Sensuous Magic* by Pat Califia.

General Information

San Francisco Sex Information. (415) 621-7300. Offers referrals and information on sex-related issues. (Note: SFSI is not a phone sex company!)

Kink Aware Professionals ("KAP") c/o Race Bannon, 584 Castro Street, Suite 518, San Francisco, CA 94114. E-Mail: 72114.2327@compuserve.com

To receive a free listing of kink-friendly psychotherapeutic, medical, dental, alternative healing, or legal professionals, send a self-addressed, stamped envelope (must have two first class stamps to cover extra postage). Or, send an e-mail message to 72114.2327@compuserve.com requesting the list. New professional listings are also always welcome.

BDSM Organizations

If you don't find a local group listed, that does not mean that one doesn't exist. *Prometheus* (see below) regularly includes a national listing of BDSM organizations and is an invaluable resource.

The Eulenspiegel Society. 212-388-7022. Box 2783, New York, NY 10163-2783. **http://www.mcsp.com/tes/welcome.html** This group has recently celebrated their 25th anniversary! They host meetings and events in the New York Metro area and publish *Prometheus*, an intelligent and entertaining quarterly magazine. All genders.

Society of Janus. 415-985-7117. Box 6794, San Francisco, CA 94101. **http://www.blackiris.com/SFLeatherMC/Janus/janus.html** Another long-standing social and support group. They host educational meetings and play parties. All genders.

Outcasts. 415-487-5170. PO Box 31266, San Francisco, CA 94131. Social and educational group with monthly meetings for women interested in S/M with other women. Lesbian, bisexual, heterosexual, and transsexual women welcome.

Pervert Scouts. 415-285-7985. 3288 21st St #19, San Francisco, CA 94110. Casual group for women into S/M. Meetings held twice a month; no membership required. Call for information.

National Leather Association. 415-863-2444. 584 Castro St. #444, San Francisco, CA 94114-2500. Pansexual group with local chapters all over the U.S.

LINKS. 415-703-7159. PO Box 420989, San Francisco, CA 94142-0989. LINKS is a social & informative network of lesbian, straight, gay, bi, young, old, queer and/or transgendered people into leather, SM, bondage, D/S, genderfuck or other fetish & power play. They publish a monthly calendar of leather events, the Leather Want Ads and annually updated directories of fetish resources. They also produce parties and other special events for the leather/fetish community. They extend their party invitations to seasoned veterans and responsible novices alike and encourage sharing of experience, techniques, resources & visions. Very TG/TS/TV-friendly.

Non-Fiction Books and Magazines

While there are innumerable mainstream porn magazines and paperbacks for the reader with an interest in BDSM, many of them only perpetuate stereotypes and do little to educate real people about real BDSM. We can only be thankful that the following companies exist.

Greenery Press. 3739 Balboa Ave. #195, San Francisco, CA 94121, **http://www.bigrock.com/~greenery**. Lady Green publishes a number of excellent introductions to BDSM, including Jay Wiseman's *SM 101*, her own *The Sexually Dominant Woman: A Workbook for Nervous Beginners*, and both *The Bottoming Book* and *The Topping Book*, co-authored by Dossie Easton and Catherine A. Liszt. These sensible and entertainingly well-written little gems are musts for your BDSM library. Also recommended is Jay Wiseman's *Personal ADventures: How to Meet Through Personal Ads*, a good introduction for individuals seeking partners. Lady Green also publishes a newsletter and teaches classes for novice dominant women and their partners. Send a SASE, or e-mail her at verdant@crl.com, for a catalog.

Diversified Services. 617-787-7426. PO Box 35737, Brighton, MA 02135. Provides a number of services, including publishing The *Mentor* Series, an excellent series of booklets on bondage, finding partners, professional domination, and more. They also have an illustrated catalog of toys, available for $2 (refundable with first order).

The Utopian Network. 516-842-1711 (M-F 11am-9pm ET). PO Box 1146, New York, NY 10156. **http://www.catalog.com/ utopian** Publishers of *The Sandmutopian Guardian* and home of Adam and Gillian's Sensual Whips and Toys. The Guardian is an excellent how-to publication ("fast becoming both the 'Popular Mechanics' and the 'Consumer Reports' of SM") concentrating on factual, useful articles rather than fiction and fantasy. Adam and Gillian's Sensual Whips and Toys makes wonderful playthings with sensations ranging from sensual to intense.

Cuir Underground. 415-487-7622. 3288 21st St #19, San Francisco, CA 94110. **http://www.black-rose.com/cuiru.html** The only newspaper for the Bay Area's pansexual kink communities. Snappy writing, hot graphics, and intelligent analysis make this paper appealing to people both in and outside of the Bay Area. Subscriptions available for $20/year. Send a signed age statement with your order.

Daedalus Publishing Company. 415-626-1867. Fax: 415-487-1137. 584 Castro Street, Suite 518, San Francisco, CA 94114. E-mail: DPCBooks@aol.com **http:/www.bookfair.com/publishers/ daedalus/macg** Daedalus Publishing Company provides quality non-fiction books on leather/SM/fetish sexuality.

Stores and Mail Order Companies

QSM. 415-550-7776. PO Box 880154, San Francisco, CA 94188. Mail order company devoted exclusively to BDSM books and magazines. The "Q" stands for quality! Reliable service and the widest selection around. Write or call for a free copy of their 20-page illustrated catalog. QSM also sponsors classes in the Bay Area. Call for information and calendar of events.

Blowfish. 415-285-6064 (M-F, 10am-5pm PT). 2261 Market St #284, San Francisco, CA 94114. **http://www.blowfish.com/** As well as having a wonderfully silly name, Blowfish is a wonderfully eclectic sex book, toy and video mail order company. Very kink-friendly. For a catalog, send $3 (refundable with order) and an 18 age statement.

Good Vibrations. 415-974-8980. 1210 Valencia St, San Francisco, CA. This venerable establishment has recently opened a second location at 2504 San Pablo Ave, Berkeley, CA 510-841-8986. A friendly, relaxed store for sex toys and books.

Stormy Leather. 415-626-1672. 1158 Howard St., San Francisco, CA 94103. Wholesale and retail leather and fetish gear. No mail order, but well worth the visit if you're in town.

Body Modification Artists

Gauntlet. 415-431-3133. 2377 Market St, San Francisco, CA 94114. Established piercing salon with several locations across the country. Well-trained and knowledgeable staff and a beautiful selection of jewelry.

Raelyn Gallina. 510-655-2855. PO Box 20034, Oakland, CA 94620. One of the Bay Area's most experienced and talented independent piercers and jewelers, Raelyn is also adept at doing body art within a ritual context. She regularly tours the country; write for information.

Fakir Musafar. 415-324-0543. c/o Insight Books, PO Box 2575, Menlo Park, CA 94026-2575. This guru of the "modern primitives" movement now runs his own piercing school. He also publishes *Body Play and Modern Primitives Quarterly,* an excellent source of information on all forms of body modification, including corseting and waist training, branding, and of course, piercing.

Professional Dominants

It would be impossible to list all of the reputable professional dominants working today. Adult newspapers, like the Bay Area's Spectator (1-800-624-8433) or the S&M News (1-717-839-2512) carry ads for independent professionals as well as houses. Dominants Directory International ("DDI" to those in the know) is a glossy quarterly with ads from dominas worldwide. The women listed below are skilled lifestyle dominants with many years of experience. I have also listed one San Francisco house with a fine reputation. These professionals provide consensual BDSM, not sex.

Mistress Cybelle. 415-558-9531. Private sessions, information and counseling by California certified sex educator. Phone sessions also available. Specializes in erotic pain, adult baby/sissy/badboy games, and total, transformational cross-dressing.

Cléo Dubois Academy of SM Arts. 415-322-0124. Private sessions, couples instruction, and consultations, demonstrations and play for unpartnered dominants. Specializes in bondage, sensory deprivation, captive games, electroplay, flagellation, corsets and canes for submissives and masochists.

Castlebar. 415-552-2100. BDSM sessions (dominant, submissive, and switch) for are available by appointment at this well-equipped San Francisco dungeon. Room rentals for private parties. Woman-owned and -run.

Therapists

These Bay Area therapists are knowledgeable and accepting of BDSM lifestyles.

Pat Califia, M.A. 415-584-4424 2215R Market St., #261 San Francisco, CA 94114 All sexual orientations and genders. Specializes in family-of-origin issues, relationships, life transitions, and recovery from addiction. If you wish a reply by mail, please enclose an SASE. All long-distance calls must be returned collect. (MFCC Intern No. 28798. Supervisor Rochelle Wald, LCS 13786)

Dossie Easton, M.A. 415-752-7455. 20 years experience. All sexual lifestyles and gender identities. Individuals and couples. Sexual concerns, depression, anxiety, and healing from child abuse.

William Henkin, Ph.D. 415-923-1150. Board Certified Sex Therapist and member of numerous professional organizations. Individuals, couples and small ménages. Specializes in alternative sex and gender concerns, including TS/TG/TV issues (Member HBIGDA). Works with alternate personalities and archetypes and intimacy and relationship issues.

Information on the Internet

These days no resource listing would be complete without World Wide Web sites. Here are a few of the most reliable and useful URLs. Note: the Internet is growing by leaps and bounds, and sites come and go quickly. Some listed here may no longer be in service.

http://www.yahoo.com/Society_and_Culture/Sexuality/ **BDSM** Yahoo maintains links to hot web sites, so having your pages linked from Yahoo is a mark of distinction on the web. An excellent starting point.

http://203.61.10.6/ LeatherWeb. An extensive listing of BDSM web sites, including a library. Another good place to start.

http://www.sfdungeon.com A commercial site featuring products by a number of Bay Area leather businesses and craftspeople.

http://www.fifth-mountain.com/radical_sex A home page that includes numerous links to other BDSM sites and an extensive book and periodical listing.

http://www.romantasy.com/cyboutique Romantasy's online boutique. Excellent information on corsetry.

http://www.circlet.com/circlet/home.html Home page of Cecilia Tan's Circlet Press, publishers of erotic science fiction and fantasy.

http://www.the-wire.com/boudoir.noir Home page of Boudoir Noir, a Canadian BDSM publication.

http://www.dungeon.com/~SkinTwo Home page of the well-known British fetish magazine.

OTHER BOOKS FROM GREENERY PRESS

BDSM/KINK

The Compleat Spanker
Lady Green $12.95

Erotic Tickling
Michael Moran $13.95

Family Jewels: A Guide to Male Genital Play
and Torment
Hardy Haberman $12.95

Flogging
Joseph W. Bean $12.95

Intimate Invasions: The Ins and Outs of
Erotic Enema Play
M.R. Strict $13.95

Jay Wiseman's Erotic Bondage Handbook
Jay Wiseman $16.95

The Kinky Girl's Guide to Dating
Luna Grey $16.95

The Loving Dominant
John Warren $16.95

The Mistress Manual
Mistress Lorelei $16.95

Radical Ecstasy: SM Journeys to Transcen-
dence
Dossie Easton & Janet W. Hardy $16.95

The Seductive Art of Japanese Bondage
Midori $27.95

The Sexually Dominant Woman: A
Workbook for Nervous Beginners
Lady Green $11.95

SM 101: A Realistic Introduction
Jay Wiseman $24.95

Training With Miss Abernathy: A Workbook
for Erotic Slaves and Their Owners
Christina Abernathy $13.95

GENERAL SEXUALITY

Big Big Love: A Sourcebook on Sex for People of
Size and Those Who Love Them
Hanne Blank $15.95

The Bride Wore Black Leather... And He
Looked Fabulous!: An Etiquette Guide for
the Rest of Us
Andrew Campbell $11.95

The Ethical Slut: A Guide to Infinite Sexual
Possibilities
Dossie Easton & Catherine A. Liszt $16.95

A Hand in the Bush: The Fine Art of
Vaginal Fisting
Deborah Addington $13.95

Health Care Without Shame: A Handbook
for the Sexually Diverse and Their Caregivers
Charles Moser, Ph.D., M.D. $11.95

Look Into My Eyes: How to Use Hypnosis to
Bring Out the Best in Your Sex Life
Peter Masters $16.95

Paying For It: A Guide By Sex Workers for
Their Customers
edited by Greta Christina $13.95

Phone Sex: Oral Thrills and Aural Skills
Miranda Austin $15.95

Photography for Perverts
Charles Gatewood $27.95

Sex Disasters... And How to Survive Them
Charles Moser, Ph.D., M.D. and Janet W.
Hardy $16.95

Tricks... To Please a Man
Tricks... To Please a Woman
both by Jay Wiseman $14.95 ea.

When Someone You Love Is Kinky
Dossie Easton & Catherine A. Liszt $15.95

TOYBAG GUIDES: A Workshop In A Book
$9.95 each

Canes and Caning, by Janet Hardy

Clips and Clamps, by Jack Rinella

Foot and Shoe Worship, by Midori

High-Tech Toys, by John Warren

Hot Wax and Temperature Play, by Spectrum

Dungeon Emergencies & Supplies, by Jay
Wiseman

FICTION

... But I Know What You Want: 25 Sex Tales
for the Different
James Williams $13.95

Love, Sal: letters from a boy in The City
Sal Iacopelli, ill. Phil Foglio $13.95

Murder At Roissy
John Warren $15.95

Haughty Spirit
The Warrior Within
The Warrior Enchained
all by Sharon Green $11.95 ea.

Please include $3 for first book and $1 for each additional book with your order to cover shipping and handling costs, plus $10 for overseas orders. VISA/MC accepted. Order from Greenery Press, 4200 Park Blvd. pmb 240, Oakland, CA 510/530-1281.